Number Concepts, Decimals and Graphs

Contents

Introduction

Building a solid foundation in math is a student's key to success in school and in the future. This book will help students to develop the basic math skills that they will use every day. As students build on math skills that they already know and learn new math skills, they will see how much math connects to real life.

This book will help students to:

- develop math competence;
- acquire basic math skills and concepts;
- learn problem-solving strategies;
- apply these skills and strategies to everyday life;
- gain confidence in their own ability to succeed at learning.

Students who have self-confidence in their math skills often do better in other school areas, too. Mastering math helps students to become better learners and better students.

Ensure Student Success in Math

This book contains several features that help teachers to build the self-confidence of math students. This book enables the teacher to:

- reach students by providing a unique approach to math content;
- help students build basic foundational math skills;
- diagnose specific math intervention needs;
- provide individualized, differentiated instruction.

Assessment. An Assessment is included to serve as a diagnostic tool. The Assessment contains most of the math concepts presented in this book. An Assessment Evaluation Chart helps to pinpoint each student's strengths and weaknesses. Then, instruction can be focused on the math content each student needs. Each item in the Assessment is linked to a lesson in the book where students can hone their math skills.

Correlation to Standards. A Correlation to NCTM Standards is provided to allow teachers to tailor their teaching to standardized tests. This chart shows teachers at a glance which lessons cover the basic skills students are expected to master.

Lesson Format. Each lesson in the book is constructed to help students master the specific concept covered in the lesson. A short introduction explains the concept. Then, a step-by-step process is used to work an example problem. Students are then given a short problem to work on their own. Finally, a page of practice problems that reinforce the concept is provided.

Glossary. Math has a language of its own, so a Glossary of math terms is included at the back of the book. Students can look up terms that confuse them, and they are directed to a specific page on which the term is explained or implemented.

Answer Key. Finally, a complete Answer Key is provided at the end of the book. The Answer Key includes the answers for the practice problems as well as explanations on how many of the answers are reached. These explanations can be useful to the teacher to explain why students might have answered incorrectly.

Working Together to Help Students Achieve

No student wants to do poorly. There are many reasons students may be having problems with math. This book presents a well-organized, straightforward approach to helping students overcome the obstacles that may hold them back. This book and your instruction can help students to regain their footing and continue their climb to math achievement.

Correlation to NCTM Standards

Content Strands   Lesson

Number and Operations

• work flexibly with fractions, decimals, and percents to solve problems	23, 24, 25, 26, 27, 28, 29
• compare and order fractions, decimals, and percents efficiently and find their approximate locations on a number line	19, 20, 21, 22
• understand and use ratios and proportions to represent quantitative relationships	41
• develop an understanding of large numbers and recognize and appropriately use exponential, scientific, and calculator notation	14, 16, 17
• use factors, multiples, prime factorization, and relatively prime numbers to solve problems	14, 15, 16, 17, 18
• develop meaning for integers and represent and compare quantities with them	1, 2, 10, 13
• understand the meaning and effects of arithmetic operations with fractions, decimals, and integers	5, 6, 7, 11, 12, 18, 23, 24, 25, 26, 27, 28
• use the associative and commutative properties of addition and multiplication and the distributive property of multiplication over addition to simplify computations with integers, fractions, and decimals	7, 8, 25
• understand and use the inverse relationships of addition and subtraction, multiplication and division, and squaring and finding square roots to simplify computations and solve problems	14, 15
• select appropriate methods and tools for computing with fractions and decimals from among mental computation, estimation, calculators or computers, and paper and pencil, depending on the situation, and apply the selected methods	3, 4, 21
• develop and analyze algorithms for computing with fractions, decimals, and integers and develop fluency in their use	5, 6, 7, 9, 11, 12, 18, 23, 24, 25, 26, 27, 28
• develop and use strategies to estimate the results of rational-number computations and judge the reasonableness of the results	4
• develop, analyze, and explain methods for solving problems involving proportions, such as scaling and finding equivalent ratios	41

Data Analysis and Probability

• formulate questions, design studies, and collect data about a characteristic shared by two populations or different characteristics within one	41
• select, create, and use appropriate graphical representations of data, including histograms, box plots, and scatter plots	30, 31, 32, 33, 34, 35, 36, 37, 38, 39, 40, 42, 43
• discuss and understand the correspondence between data sets and their graphical representations, especially histograms, stem-and-leaf plots, box plots, and scatter plots	31, 33, 35, 37, 38, 39, 40, 42, 43
• use observations about differences between two or more samples to make conjectures about the populations from which the samples were taken	40, 41
• make conjectures about possible relationships between two characteristics of a sample on the basis of scatter plots of the data and approximate lines of fit	37

Assessment

Take this Assessment before you begin this book. Do not worry if you cannot easily answer all the questions. The Assessment will help you determine which skills you are already strong in and which skills you need to practice.

1. Write 185,405 in words. _____

2. Write the value of the underlined digit in 215,706. _____

Compare. Use > or <.

3. 40,654 ☐ 40,574   **4.** −2 ☐ −3   **5.** −6 ☐ −4 ☐ 0

6. Round 147,524 to the value of the underlined digit. _____

Answer each question. Use estimation to make sure your answer is reasonable.

7. The sporting goods store sold 950 pairs of gym socks and 260 pairs of sunglasses during a 3-hour sale. About how many socks and sunglasses were sold in all?

8. During a canned-food drive, the freshman class brought in 860 cans of food. The sophomore class brought in 725 cans. About how many more cans did the freshman class bring in than the sophomore class?

Solve.

9. $4,309 + 705 =$ _____   **10.** $1,308 - 129 =$ _____

11. $-14 + 6 =$ _____   **12.** $-14 - 6 =$ _____

13. In a math game, Darnell scored 6 points. On his next play, he lost 8 points. What was Darnell's total score after two plays?

14. Use the distributive property. Let A = 6, B = 30, and C = 4. A(B + C) =

4

Solve.

15. $32 \times 219 =$ _____

16. $1,458 \div 27 =$ _____

17. $45 \div (-5) =$ _____

18. $-6 \times (-8) =$ _____

19. The temperature falls by 2°F each day for 10 days. What is the total change in temperature after ten days?

20. The trip from Chantal's house to her grandparents' home is 945 miles. Every hour she drives 50 miles. How many hours will Chantal have to drive to get to their house?

Find the absolute value for each integer.

21. $|-22|$ _____

22. $|9|$ _____

Solve.

23. $8^2 =$ _____

24. $\sqrt{49} =$ _____

25. $4^3 =$ _____

26. $6^5 \times 6^9 =$ _____

Write the decimal.

27. 45 and 46 hundredths

28. 3 and 71 thousandths

_____

_____

29. 16 and 19 thousandths

30. 6 hundred 5 thousandths

_____

_____

What is the value of the underlined digit?

31. 978.2<u>1</u> _____

32. 59.<u>3</u>97 _____

33. 78.7<u>1</u>3 _____

Round each decimal to the nearest tenth.

34. 0.474

35. 17.518

36. 0.995

_____

_____

_____

Compare. Use <, >, or = sign.

37. 0.378 ☐ 0.48

38. 7.379 ☐ 7.37

39. 0.72 ☐ 1.7

Order the decimals from least to greatest.

40. 1.9 0.19 0.109 0.91 _____

41. 47.52 47.500 47.05 47.205 _____

Add or subtract.

42. 6.465 + 143.78 = _____

43. 9.003 + 18.34 = _____

44. 7.45 − 3.76 = _____

45. 32.9 − 6.37 = _____

Multiply or divide.

46. 30.6 × 3 = _____

47. 320 ÷ 0.4 = _____

48. 0.62 × 42 = _____

49. 3,864 ÷ 9.2 = _____

Change each decimal to a fraction or fraction to a decimal.

50. 0.75 _____

51. $\frac{7}{10}$ _____

52. 0.9 _____

53. $\frac{3}{100}$ _____

Solve.

54. An athlete runs a mile in 8.4 minutes. If he runs at the same speed for 5 miles, how long will it take him?

55. If a person has $609.88 in his savings account and withdraws $145.90, how much is left?

Use the double line graph to answer questions 56 and 57.

56. During which season do teenage boys spend more time learning to drive than teenage girls?

_____

57. During which season do teenage boys and teenage girls spend about the same number of hours learning to drive?

_____

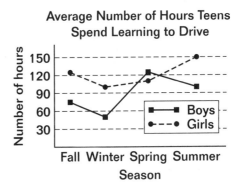

Average Number of Hours Teens Spend Learning to Drive

Use the double bar graph to answer questions 58 and 59.

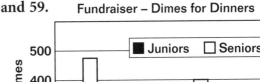

Fundraiser – Dimes for Dinners

58. Which month did the seniors bring in twice as many dimes as the juniors?

_____

59. Which month did the juniors bring in the most dimes?

_____

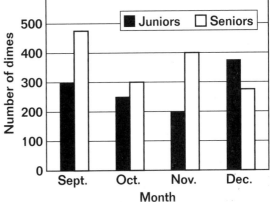

Use the circle graph to answer questions 60 and 61.

Medals Won by China at the 2004 Summer Olympics

Bronze 14

Gold 32

Silver 17

60. About $\frac{1}{2}$ of China's medals were what color?

_____

61. Which color medal was less than 25% of China's medals?

_____

Use the scatter plot to answer questions 62–64.

62. About how much money does a teen who makes less than $200 per week save?

_____

63. About how much money does a teen save if he or she makes $300 or more per week?

_____

64. True or false, the more money teens earn the more money they save? Explain.

_____

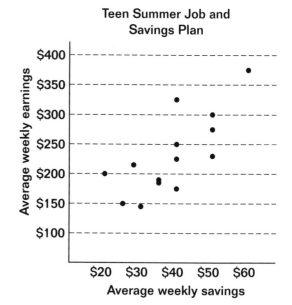

Teen Summer Job and Savings Plan

Average weekly earnings

$400
$350
$300
$250
$200
$150
$100

$20 $30 $40 $50 $60

Average weekly savings

Name _____   Date _____

Assessment Evaluation Chart

Circle the number of each assessment item that you missed. Then use the Lesson Review list to find more practice problems.

ITEM NUMBER	LESSON FOR REVIEW	ITEM NUMBER	LESSON FOR REVIEW
1	Lesson 1	33	Lesson 19
2	Lesson 2	34	Lesson 21
3	Lesson 2	35	Lesson 21
4	Lesson 10	36	Lesson 21
5	Lesson 10	37	Lesson 22
6	Lesson 3	38	Lesson 22
7	Lesson 4	39	Lesson 22
8	Lesson 4	40	Lesson 22
9	Lesson 5	41	Lesson 22
10	Lesson 6	42	Lesson 23
11	Lesson 11	43	Lesson 23
12	Lesson 11	44	Lesson 24
13	Lesson 6	45	Lesson 24
14	Lesson 8	46	Lesson 25
15	Lesson 7	47	Lesson 27
16	Lesson 9	48	Lesson 25
17	Lesson 12	49	Lesson 27
18	Lesson 12	50	Lesson 29
19	Lesson 12	51	Lesson 29
20	Lesson 9	52	Lesson 29
21	Lesson 13	53	Lesson 29
22	Lesson 13	54	Lesson 25
23	Lesson 14	55	Lesson 24
24	Lesson 15	56	Lessons 30, 31
25	Lesson 16	57	Lessons 30, 31
26	Lesson 17	58	Lessons 32, 33
27	Lesson 20	59	Lessons 32, 33
28	Lesson 20	60	Lesson 34
29	Lesson 20	61	Lesson 34
30	Lesson 20	62	Lesson 37
31	Lesson 19	63	Lesson 37
32	Lesson 19	64	Lesson 37

Assessment
Number Concepts, Decimals, and Graphs, SV 0435-2

Date _____

LESSON 1 Reading and Writing Whole Numbers

Place value can help you read and write whole numbers. There are three ways to show a whole number. In standard form, you use just the numerals, for example, 753. The word form is how you say the number, seven hundred fifty-three. In **expanded form,** you write out all the place values separately, for example, 700 + 50 + 3.

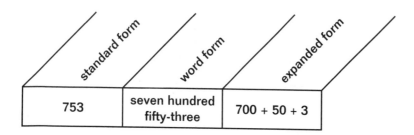

standard form	word form	expanded form
753	seven hundred fifty-three	700 + 50 + 3

Example

Write the value of the underlined digit in 324,516.

STEP 1 Draw and label a place-value chart.

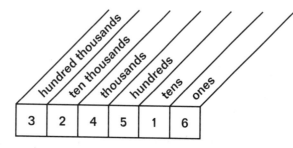

hundred thousands	ten thousands	thousands	hundreds	tens	ones
3	2	4	5	1	6

STEP 2 Write the digits in the chart, beginning with the ones place.

STEP 3 Write the digit and name of the place.
4 thousands

The value of 4 in 324,516 is 4 thousand.

(ON YOUR OWN)

The land area for the state of Arizona is 295,260 square kilometers. What is the value of 9 in 295,260?

Number Concepts, Decimals, and Graphs, SV 0435-2

Practice

Building Skills

Write each number in word form.

1. 28,175 _____

2. 215,125 _____

Write the number.

3. fifty-four thousand one hundred sixty _____

4. four hundred five thousand six hundred twenty-seven _____

5. one hundred seventy-five thousand nine hundred forty-six _____

Write the value of the underlined digit.

6. 2<u>1</u>,361 _____   **7.** <u>8</u>07,205 _____

8. 45,7<u>5</u>8 _____   **9.** 75,0<u>1</u>3 _____

Problem Solving

Write the number in word form or expanded form.

10. The bank reported that 125,345 customers visited the bank in the past year. How is this number written in words?

_____

11. On the opening day of a movie, 8,542,349 people from across the country saw the movie. How do you write this number in words?

_____

12. Officials predict that the population of Michigan will be 9,763,000 by the year 2015. How would you write this population in expanded form?

_____

13. The number of cars sold in a state was 1,030,402. How would you write this number in expanded form?

_____

Find the value of the digit. Use a place-value chart.

14. Russia covers 6,592,735 square miles. What is the value of the 9 in 6,592,735?

_____

15. The Mall of America in Minneapolis, Minnesota, covers 4,200,000 square feet. What is the value of the 2 in 4,200,000?

_____

LESSON ② Comparing and Ordering Whole Numbers

When you compare and order whole numbers, the whole number with more digits is always greater. If the number of digits is the same, you begin by comparing the digits in the greatest place-value position. If those digits are the same, you move one place to the right and compare the digits there. When you find a place-value position where the digits are different, you know that the greater digit is in the greater number.

NOTE: If all of the digits are the same, then the numbers are equal.

ten thousands	thousands	hundreds	tens	ones
6	8	2	1	5
6	8	3	0	7

Example

Which number is greater, 68,215 or 68,307?

STEP 1 Line up the numbers by place value.
You can use a place-value chart to help you.

STEP 2 Compare digits, starting on the left. When you find two different digits in the same place-value position, underline them.

68,215
68,307

STEP 3 Compare the underlined digits.
3 > 2, so 68,307 > 68,215.

68,307 is greater than 68,215.

(ON YOUR OWN)

Which number is greater, 402,682 or 402,197?

Practice

Begin comparing digits in the greatest place value.

Building Skills

Compare each pair of numbers. Use $<$, $>$, or $=$.

1. 647 ☐ 592   **2.** 536 ☐ 563   **3.** 872 ☐ 827

4. 2,759 ☐ 2,765   **5.** 3,152 ☐ 3,025   **6.** 1,024 ☐ 1,127

7. 6,139 ☐ 6,029   **8.** 25,094 ☐ 26,303   **9.** 512,057 ☐ 512,750

Problem Solving

Solve.

10. The flight distance from Kansas City, Missouri, to Boston, Massachusetts, is 1,251 miles. The distance from Memphis, Tennessee, to Boston is 1,137 miles. Which distance is greater?

11. Scientists measure the length of two of the largest lakes in Canada. One lake is 232 miles long. The other lake is 298 miles long. Which lake is longer?

12. The attendance at the college women's basketball championship was 29,619 in 2002. Attendance in 2003 was 28,210. Which year had the lower attendance?

13. The Robinson family drove 1,703 miles on their summer vacation. The Duval family drove 1,730 miles on theirs. Which family drove farther?

14. Yuri scored 54,076 points playing a video game. Tony scored 54,067 points. Who scored more points?

15. Jason collected 534 bottles and cans for charity. His sister Meg collected 543. Who collected more?

_____ Date _____

LESSON ③ **Rounding**

Sometimes you only need to know *about how many,* not an actual number. When problems ask for *about how many,* use rounding. Rounding also makes problems easier to solve.

When rounding, look at the digit to the right of the place you're rounding to. This is the rounding number.

- If the rounding number is 5 or greater, round up.
- If the rounding number is less than 5, round down.

The following shows 48,279 rounded to three different place values.

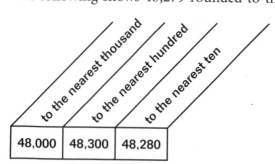

to the nearest thousand	to the nearest hundred	to the nearest ten
48,000	48,300	48,280

Example

What is 26,379 rounded to the nearest hundred?

STEP 1 **Find the digit in the place value you want to round to and circle it.**
The digit 3 is in the hundreds position.

26,③79

STEP 2 **Underline the rounding digit.**
7 is to the right of 3.

26,③7̲9

STEP 3 **If the rounding digit is 5 or greater, add one to the circled digit. If the rounding digit is less than 5, do not change the circled digit. Replace the digits to the right of the circled digit with zeros.**
The underlined digit is 7. It is greater than 5.

4
26,③7̲9
400
26,⑨79 → 26,400

26,379 rounded to the nearest hundred is 26,400.

(ON YOUR OWN)

What is 47,591 rounded to the nearest hundred?

Practice

Building Skills

Round to the underlined place.

1. 342 _____

2. 1,357 _____

3. 515 _____

4. 735 _____

5. 4,382 _____

6. 371 _____

7. 854 _____

8. 12,138 _____

9. 6,308 _____

10. 42,574 _____

11. 1,639 _____

12. 57,186 _____

Problem Solving

Round each number.

13. California's Golden Gate Bridge is 8,981 feet long. What is its length rounded to the nearest thousand?

_____

14. At 19,340 feet, the peak of Mount Kilimanjaro is the highest point in Africa. What is its height to the nearest hundred?

_____

15. The Statue of Liberty is 305 feet tall. What is its height rounded to the nearest ten?

_____

16. The Nile River is 4,160 miles long. What is its length rounded to the nearest hundred?

_____

17. The CN Tower in Toronto, Canada, has the world's longest metal staircase, with 2,579 steps. What is the number of steps rounded to the nearest ten?

_____

18. The world's largest cruise ship is the *Queen Mary 2*. It is 1,132 feet long. What is its length to the nearest hundred?

_____

LESSON ④ Estimation

Sometimes it is not necessary to get exact answers to a problem. An approximate answer is good enough. You use estimation to get approximate answers. Instead of using exact numbers, you use numbers that are close enough to do the job. Here are the three main ways to estimate.

Type of estimation	What it is	Examples
Front-end estimation	Use the leading digits. The leading digit is the first digit on the left. Change the rest of the digits to 0s.	$782 \longrightarrow 700$ $- \overline{4}19 \longrightarrow 400$ $\overline{300}$
Rounding	Round numbers usually to the highest place before calculating.	$419 \longrightarrow 400$ $+ 263 \longrightarrow 300$ $\overline{700}$
Compatible numbers	Change numbers to make the calculation easy. You can round up or down for any place value.	$144 \longrightarrow 150$ $+ 157 \longrightarrow 150$ $\overline{300}$

Example

Use front-end estimation to estimate $5,325 + 1,815$.

STEP 1 Circle the leading digits.

⑤,325 + ①,815

STEP 2 Rewrite the numbers using the leading digits.

$5,000 + 1,000$

STEP 3 Solve.

$5,000 + 1,000 = 6,000$

$5,325 + 1,815$ is about $6,000$.

ON YOUR OWN

Use front-end estimation to estimate $3,862 - 1,710$.

Practice

Round each number to the same place value.

Building Skills

Solve each problem using front-end estimation.

1. 4,357 + 162 _____   **2.** 821 − 372 _____

Solve each problem using rounding. Round to the nearest hundred or thousand.

3. 317 + 692 _____   **4.** 638 − 172 _____

5. 1,670 + 1,138 _____   **6.** 3,752 − 1,408 _____

Solve each problem using compatible numbers.

7. 19 + 22 _____   **8.** 88 + 12 _____

9. 173 + 128 _____   **10.** 262 + 578 _____

Problem Solving

Use rounding to solve these problems.

11. The Sears Tower in Chicago has 110 stories. The Chrysler Building in New York has 77 stories. About how many more stories does the Sears Tower have than the Chrysler Building?

_____

12. Results from the student elections showed that Marcus received 475 votes from the freshman class and 319 votes from the sophomore class. About how many votes did Marcus receive from the two classes altogether?

_____

13. The attendance at a city swimming pool was 54,861 in July and 52,015 in August. About how much greater was the attendance in July?

_____

14. Peter walks dogs. On Monday, he walks 5 dogs. On Tuesday, he walks 4 dogs. He walks each dog for almost 1 hour. About how many hours does Peter work?

_____

15. The weight of an elephant is 11,990 pounds. A bear weighs 1,595 pounds. About how much more does the elephant weigh than the bear?

_____

16. Over the weekend 628 people attended one volleyball game, and 565 people attended another. About how many people attended the games over the weekend?

_____

Name _____ Date _____

LESSON 5 Adding Whole Numbers

Keeping the place-value chart in mind helps you to remember how to line up digits when you add. Sometimes you will have to regroup numbers to the next place value. On tests, addition problems may be arranged in columns or in rows.

Example

Add. 825 + 579

STEP 1 Line up the digits by place value.

```
 H T O
 8 2 5
+5 7 9
```

STEP 2 Add the ones. Regroup if necessary.
5 + 9 = 14 ones.
Regroup 14 as 1 ten and 4 ones.

```
   1 ←———— 1 ten
 8 2 5
+5 7 9
     4 ←———— 4 ones
```

STEP 3 Add the tens column. Regroup if necessary.
2 + 7 + 1 = 10. Write 0 in the tens column.
Regroup 1 to the hundreds column.

```
 1 1
 8 2 5
+5 7 9
   0 4
```

STEP 4 Add the hundreds. Regroup if necessary.
If there are ten or more hundreds, regroup the 1 to the thousands place.

```
 1 1
 8 2 5
+5 7 9
1 4 0 4
```

825 + 579 = 1,404

ON YOUR OWN

Last summer, Melissa traveled 748 miles with her family from Atlanta to New York. Then they traveled 215 miles from New York to Boston. How many miles did they travel in all?

Practice

Building Skills

Add.

1. 532 + 159 =

2. 2,403 + 829 =

3. 812 + 249 =

4. 2,147 + 315 =

5. 214 + 639 =

6. 315 + 179 =

7. 786 + 457 =

8. 3,075 + 542 =

9. 1,892 + 248 =

Problem Solving

Add.

10. The Strawberry Festival organizers handed out samples of strawberries during the festival. On the first day, they gave out 1,835 pounds of samples. On the second day, they handed out 891 pounds of samples. How many pounds of strawberries were handed out as samples?

11. Markus scored 1,235 points in the first half of a video game. He scored 784 points in the second half of the game. What was his total score?

12. Caleb used his cell phone for 234 minutes in one week. He used 268 minutes the second week. How many minutes was Caleb talking on his cell phone during this two-week period?

13. Tara has 137 CDs. Frank has 53 CDs. How many CDs do Tara and Frank own?

14. At a local park, the high school biology club planted 1,464 lilies and 1,374 wildflowers. How many flowers did they plant?

15. On Friday, 873 people attended the school play. On Saturday, 1,273 people attended. What was the total attendance for the two shows?

Name _____   Date _____

LESSON 6 Subtracting Whole Numbers

As in addition, to solve a subtraction problem, you line up digits by place value.

Sometimes it looks like you have to subtract a larger digit from a smaller one. When this happens, you have to regroup.

Example

Subtract. 645 − 162

STEP 1 Line up the digits by place value.

$$\begin{array}{r} 6\,4\,5 \\ -\,1\,6\,2 \\ \hline \end{array}$$

STEP 2 Subtract the ones. Regroup if necessary.

$$\begin{array}{r} 6\,4\,5 \\ -\,1\,6\,2 \\ \hline 3 \end{array}$$

STEP 3 Subtract the tens. Regroup if necessary.
You cannot subtract 6 from 4. Regroup 1 hundred as 10 tens. This gives you 14 in the tens column. This leaves 5 hundreds in the hundreds column.

$$\begin{array}{r} \overset{5\;14}{\cancel{6}\,4\,5} \\ -\,1\,6\,2 \\ \hline 8\,3 \end{array}$$

STEP 4 Subtract the hundreds.

645 − 162 = 483

$$\begin{array}{r} \overset{5\;14}{\cancel{6}\,4\,5} \\ -\,1\,6\,2 \\ \hline 4\,8\,3 \end{array}$$

(**ON YOUR OWN**)

A five-day bicycle trip takes the riders 225 miles. The group has already traveled 78 miles. How much farther do they have to ride?

Number Concepts, Decimals, and Graphs, SV 0435-2

Name _____ Date _____

Practice

Building Skills

Subtract.

1. $872 - 128 =$ **2.** $1,629 - 348 =$ **3.** $706 - 129 =$

4. $513 - 89 =$ **5.** $538 - 175 =$ **6.** $435 - 239 =$

7. $731 - 175 =$ **8.** $1,247 - 309 =$ **9.** $3,428 - 759 =$

Problem Solving

Subtract.

10. The drama club had 692 tickets to sell for the school play. Only 64 tickets are left to sell at the door. How many tickets have the students sold?

11. Tran's volunteer team went to 345 houses to collect money for a hospital. His team visited 63 houses more than Scott's team visited. How many houses did Scott's team visit?

12. The driving distance from Jake's house to his grandparents' house is 248 miles. So far, Jake and his dad have traveled 179 miles. How many more miles do they have to go?

13. Maria has 450 stamps in her stamp collection. She has 219 stamps with pictures of animals on them. How many stamps does Maria have that do not show pictures of animals?

14. The Jacoby family cell phone plan includes 1,050 minutes per month. So far this month, they have used 628 minutes. How many more minutes do they have left for the rest of the month?

15. Azim's high school had 800 T-shirts to sell for a fund-raiser. They sold all but 189 T-shirts. How many T-shirts were sold?

LESSON 7 Multiplying Whole Numbers

To do multiplication, you must use the basic multiplication facts. You must also remember to line up all digits by their place value.

Example

Multiply. 217×23

STEP 1 Line up the digits by place value.

$$\begin{array}{r} 2\,1\,7 \\ \times 2\,3 \end{array}$$

STEP 2 Multiply by the ones digit in the bottom number.
Line up the answer numbers by place value, starting in the ones place.

$$\begin{array}{r} {\scriptstyle 2} \\ 2\,1\,7 \\ \times 2\,3 \\ \hline 6\,5\,1 \end{array}$$

STEP 3 Multiply by the tens digit in the bottom number.
Because you are beginning in the tens column, put a 0 in the ones place as a placeholder. Write that answer next to the 0, starting in the tens place.

$$\begin{array}{r} {\scriptstyle 1} \\ 2\,1\,7 \\ \times 2\,3 \\ \hline 6\,5\,1 \\ 4\,3\,4\,0 \end{array}$$

STEP 4 Add the partial products.

$217 \times 23 = 4{,}991$

$$\begin{array}{r} 217 \\ \times 23 \\ \hline 651 \\ +4340 \\ \hline 4991 \end{array}$$

ON YOUR OWN

Maya has a newspaper route. She delivers 78 newspapers per week. How many newspapers does she deliver in 25 weeks?

Name _____   Date _____

Practice

Building Skills

Multiply.

1. $52 \times 36 =$

2. $24 \times 16 =$

3. $91 \times 43 =$

4. $34 \times 28 =$

5. $326 \times 12 =$

6. $140 \times 74 =$

7. $308 \times 26 =$

8. $352 \times 24 =$

9. $106 \times 39 =$

Problem Solving

Use multiplication to solve these problems.

10. The sophomore class is selling hats that have a class logo sewn on them. They ordered 36 boxes of hats with 16 hats in each box. How many hats did they order?

11. Lyndell sent 38 instant messages on the computer every day for 17 days in a row. How many instant messages did he send?

12. The manager of a new office building needs to order one network connection for each office. The building is 15 stories high, and there are 18 offices on each floor. How many network connections should the manager order?

13. Serena has 431 plastic pieces in a model kit that will make one classic car. How many plastic pieces does she need if she wants to make 65 model cars?

Name _____ Date _____

LESSON 8 The Distributive Property

The **distributive property** looks like this:

$$A(B + C) = AB + AC$$

You read the distributive property like this:

A times B plus C equals A times B plus A times C.

In other words, multiplying *B plus C* by *A* is the same as multiplying both *C and B* by *A* and then adding the two products together.

To see how the distributive property works in action, plug in some numbers.

Let A = 2, B = 3 and C = 1:

$$A(B + C) = AB + AC$$
$$2(3 + 1) = (2 \times 3) + (2 \times 1)$$
$$2(4) = 6 + 2$$
$$8 = 8$$

Example

Use the distributive property. Let A = 6, B = 50, and C = 2.

STEP 1 Write the property.

$$A(B + C) = AB + AC$$

STEP 2 Replace the letters with numbers.
Let A = 6, B = 50 and C = 2:

$$6(50 + 2) = (6 \times 50) + (6 \times 2)$$

STEP 3 Solve.

$$6(50 + 2) = (6 \times 50) + (6 \times 2)$$
$$6(52) = 300 + 12$$
$$312 = 312$$

(ON YOUR OWN)

Use the distributive property. Let A = 4, B = 5, and C = 20.

Practice

Building Skills

Solve using the distributive property.

1. Let A = 9, B = 20, C = 4.

2. Let A = 7, B = 10, C = 5.

3. Let A = 6, B = 30, C = 3.

4. Let A = 3, B = 5, C = 20.

5. Let A = 9, B = 6, C = 10.

6. Let A = 8, B = 10, C = 4.

7. 5×27, Let A = 5, B = 20, C = 7.

8. 4×36, Let A = 4, B = 30, C = 6.

9. 8×26, Let A = 8, B = 20, C = 6.

10. 9×23, Let A = 9, B = 20, C = 3.

Problem Solving

Use the distributive property to solve these problems.

11. The local outdoor club hiked 18 miles per day on their 3-day hiking trip. How far did they hike on the trip?

12. Carlos keeps all of his CDs in 4 cases. Each case holds 28 CDs. How many CDs does Carlos have?

13. Delia found 43 packages of freeze-dried soup packets in the kitchen cabinet. Each packet can make 2 cups of soup. How many total cups of soup could Delia make with her soup packets?

14. Kelly averaged 8 points per game during the basketball season. She played in 17 games. How many points did she score during the season?

15. A cow produced 42 pints of milk each day for 9 days in a row. How many pints of milk did the cow produce?

16. Dixon completed 3 math worksheets. Each worksheet has 24 problems. How many problems did Dixon complete?

LESSON 9 Dividing Whole Numbers

You know the basic multiplication facts, so mastering division should be easy. Instead of multiplying to find a total, you divide to split a total into equal groups.

Example

Ada's car can travel 28 miles on one gallon of gas.
How many gallons of gas will the car use on a trip of 644 miles?

STEP 1 Set up the problem.
Ask yourself the question using only numbers. *How many 28s are there in 644?*

$$28\overline{)644}$$

STEP 2 Divide. Use rounding to help estimate the answer.
$28 \rightarrow 30$
$64 \rightarrow 60$ How many 30s are in 60? 2

Write 2 above the first 4.

$$\begin{array}{r} 2 \\ 28\overline{)644} \\ -56 \end{array}$$

STEP 3 Multiply.
$2 \times 28 = 56$
Subtract 56 from 64.
Bring down the next digit, 4.

$$\begin{array}{r} 2 \\ 28\overline{)644} \\ -56\downarrow \\ \hline 84 \end{array}$$

STEP 4 Divide. Use rounding to help estimate the answer.
Write 3 above the next 4. Multiply. Subtract.

The process ends when there are no more digits to bring down.

Ada's car will use 23 gallons of gas on a trip of 644 miles.

$$\begin{array}{r} 23 \\ 28\overline{)644} \\ -56 \\ \hline 84 \\ 84 \\ \hline 0 \end{array}$$

ON YOUR OWN

A bus that runs between a city and a beach area holds 65 people when all the seats are taken. How many bus trips would it take to carry a total of 1,235 people from the city to the beach?

Practice

Building Skills

Divide.

1. $2,385 \div 53 =$

2. $504 \div 21 =$

3. $3,225 \div 25 =$

4. $38\overline{)836}$

5. $81\overline{)729}$

6. $3,956 \div 23 =$

7. $63\overline{)1,827}$

8. $34\overline{)3,876}$

9. $8,118 \div 41 =$

Problem Solving

Use division to solve these problems.

10. Breadsticks are packaged 15 per box. The factory bakes 645 breadsticks an hour. How many boxes of breadsticks can the factory fill in 1 hour?

11. The soccer team played 22 games, and every game was a sellout. The team sold 3,850 tickets altogether. How many tickets did they sell for each game?

12. Malik plans to hike 18 miles per day on his hiking trip. The trail is 198 miles long. How many days will Malik need to hike to finish the entire trail?

13. Fusion Jazz has 12 performances a year at Club Artiste. The club estimates that they will sell a total of 3,960 tickets. How many tickets does the club expect to sell for each performance?

www.harcourtschoolsupply.com
27
Lesson 9
Number Concepts, Decimals, and Graphs, SV 0435-2

Name _____ Date _____

LESSON ⑩ Comparing and Ordering Integers

A number line helps you picture the order of integers. You can compare and order integers using a number line.

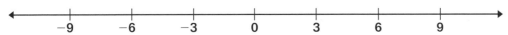

Example

Compare using $<$, $>$, or $=$. -9 ☐ -6

STEP 1 **Draw a number line and mark the numbers on it.**
When you create a number line, look at the numbers you are given and find a number that you can divide into each given number. For 9 and 6, you can use 3. You can mark your number line in intervals of 3.

> On a number line the numbers to the right of the zero are **positive numbers.** The numbers to the left of the zero are **negative numbers.**

STEP 2 **Mark the location of the numbers on the number line.**
Place a dot on the tic marks for -9 and for -6 on the number line.

STEP 3 **Compare the locations of the numbers on the number line. The number to the right is greater.**
Because -6 is to the right of -9, -6 is greater than -9.

STEP 4 **Using $<$ or $>$, write the statement comparing the two numbers.**
$-9 < -6$

(ON YOUR OWN)

The average January temperature in Fairbanks, Alaska, is -12 degrees Fahrenheit. The average January temperature in Duluth, Minnesota, is -1 degree Fahrenheit. Which city has a lower average temperature?

Practice

Building Skills

Compare each pair of integers. Write $<$ or $>$ in the ☐.

1. -12 ☐ -23 **2.** 0 ☐ -8 **3.** 5 ☐ 15

4. -5 ☐ -4 **5.** -25 ☐ 25 **6.** $+3$ ☐ -1

Use $<$ and $>$ to order these integers.

7. $7, -6,$ and 9 **8.** $-12, -5,$ and -8

9. $0, -5,$ and -14 **10.** $25, -4,$ and 0

Problem Solving

Compare integers to solve each problem.

11. When Brian and Aki started skating, the temperature was 16°F. By the time they left the rink, the temperature was 8°F. Was it colder or warmer when they left the rink?

12. Mario's final score on a game show was -250. Tanya's final score was 75. Who had the higher score?

13. During the soccer season, Matt scored 4 goals. His teammate Raphael scored 3 goals. Who scored more goals?

14. On the first math test, John missed 3 questions. On the second math test, he missed 2 questions and got 1 Bonus Question correct. On which test did he miss fewer questions?

15. In the first half of a football game, Leshon ran for -39 yards. In the second half, Leshon ran for -7 yards. In which half did Leshon have a better performance?

16. The Empire State Building in New York is 1,250 feet tall. The Sears Tower in Chicago is 1,450 feet tall. The Jin Mao Building in Shanghai, China, is 1,381 feet tall. Which building is the tallest?

Name _____ Date _____

LESSON ⑪ Adding and Subtracting Integers

You know how to display integers on a number line. You also can use the number line to add and subtract integers.

Example

Add. $-7 + (-3)$

STEP 1 Draw a number line.

STEP 2 Mark the first integer on the number line.
Put a dot on the tic mark for -7 on the number line.

STEP 3 Move the dot on the number line in the direction being added or subtracted.
When adding an integer, you move the dot in the direction of the sign of the second integer.

If the second integer is positive, move the dot to the right. If the second integer is negative, move the dot to the left.

The second number, -3, is negative. You move the dot to the left.

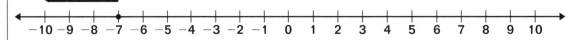

When subtracting integers, move the dot in the **opposite** direction of the second number's sign. If the second integer is positive, move the point in the negative direction, to the left. If the second integer is negative, move the point to the right.

STEP 4 Mark the place on the number line for the answer.
Move the dot 3 places to the left, to -10.

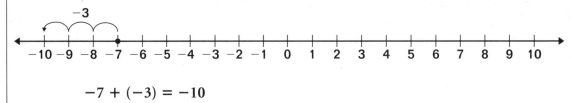

$-7 + (-3) = -10$

(ON YOUR OWN)

Subtract. $-7 - (-3)$

Practice

Adding a negative integer is the same as subtracting a positive integer.
$+ (-6) = -6$
Subtracting a negative integer is the same as adding a positive integer.
$- (-6) = +6$

Building Skills

Add or subtract.

1. $-3 - (-6) =$

2. $7 + (-2) =$

3. $-6 + (-4) =$

4. $6 + (-4) =$

5. $7 - (-5) =$

6. $-7 - (-5) =$

7. $-7 + 5 =$

8. $6 + (-8) =$

9. $-6 + (-8) =$

10. $-6 - (-8) =$

Problem Solving

Add or subtract integers to solve these problems.

11. A diver was 5 feet below the surface of the water. He then descended another 6 feet. How far below the surface was he?

12. In the first round of a golf game, Jake was 3 strokes under par, or -3. In the second round, Jake was 2 strokes over par, or $+2$. What was Jake's score after two rounds?

13. The temperature was $-2°$F at 7 A.M. By 9 A.M. it was 5°F. How much did the temperature change?

14. On Monday, Manuel recorded a windchill of $-60°$F. On Tuesday the windchill was $-45°$F. Based on windchill, which day was cooler?

15. The surface of Lake Assal in Djibouti (a country in Africa) is 156 meters below sea level. The surface of Lake Eyre in Australia is 12 meters below sea level. How much lower is Lake Assal?

16. Jeaninne used a 60-minute blank CD to record her favorite songs. One of her favorite songs is 3 minutes long, and another is 4 minutes long. How much playing time will be left on her CD after Jeaninne records these songs?

Name _____   Date _____

LESSON 12 Multiplying and Dividing Integers

You have learned how to multiply and divide whole numbers. To multiply or divide integers, you can take what you have learned about multiplication and division of whole numbers and apply a few simple rules.

> The product or quotient of two integers with the **same** sign is **positive**.
>
> The product or quotient of two integers with **different** signs is **negative**.

Example

A submarine dives at -30 feet per minute. If the submarine started at the surface of the ocean, what is the submarine's depth after 9 minutes?

STEP 1 Write the numbers with no positive or negative signs.   `30   9`

STEP 2 Multiply or divide. $30 \times 9 = 270$

STEP 3 Determine the sign of your answer.
The two integers in this problem have different signs. The answer is a negative integer.

$$-30 \times 9 = -270 \text{ feet}$$

Multiplying Integers:

$+ \times + = +$
$+ \times - = -$
$- \times + = -$
$- \times - = +$

Dividing Integers:

$+ \div + = +$
$+ \div - = -$
$- \div + = -$
$- \div - = +$

ON YOUR OWN

The depth of a diver starting at the surface of the water changed -5 feet per minute. How deep was the diver after 12 minutes?

Number Concepts, Decimals, and Graphs, SV 0435-2

Practice

Building Skills

Multiply or divide.

1. $-12 \times (-3) =$

2. $12 \times (-3) =$

3. $-3 \times (20) =$

4. $-3 \times (-20) =$

5. $-15 \div 5 =$

6. $-15 \div (-5) =$

7. $15 \div (-5) =$

8. $24 \div (-6) =$

9. $-6 \times (-4) =$

10. $-24 \div (-6) =$

Problem Solving

Multiply or divide.

11. A hot-air balloon descends at a rate of 12 feet per minute. How many feet will the balloon descend in 5 minutes?

12. The community swimming pool is being drained for the winter. The pool drains at a rate of 20 gallons per minute. How many gallons are drained in 10 minutes?

13. The new indoor community pool is being filled at a rate of 25 gallons per minute. How much water will be in the new pool after 8 minutes?

14. Jana bought 15 new CDs every month. How many CDs will Jana have in a 6-month period?

15. On a scouting trip, the temperature dropped at a rate of 3°F per hour. How many degrees did the temperature fall in an 8-hour period?

16. Sonja played great golf on the last three holes of the course. She was 2 strokes under par (-2 strokes per hole) on each hole. What was Sonja's score for these 3 holes?

Name _____   Date _____

LESSON 13 Absolute Value

The **absolute value** of a number is its distance from 0. The symbol for absolute value is | |. The absolute value of a number is always a positive number (or 0).

Look at 4 and −4 on the number line below.

The distance from 0 to 4 is 4. The distance from 0 to −4 is also 4. Therefore, the absolute value of 4 is 4 and the absolute value of −4 is 4.

$|4| = 4$ and $|-4| = 4$

Suppose you are asked to compare the absolute values of two integers. You compare the values after you have removed any negative symbols inside the absolute value symbols and the absolute value symbol.

Compare $|-6|$ and $|3|$.

First you find that $|-6|$ is 6 and $|3|$ is 3.

Because $6 > 3$, $|-6| > |3|$.

Example

Compare $|2|$ and $|-4|$. Use $>$, $<$, or $=$.

STEP 1 Delete the sign inside the absolute value symbols.
$|2|$ $|4|$

STEP 2 Delete the absolute value symbols.
2   4

STEP 3 Compare.
2 is less than 4.

2 < 4

STEP 4 Rewrite the original absolute values using $>$, $<$, or $=$ from STEP 3. the symbol for *less than* is $<$.

$|2| < |-4|$

(ON YOUR OWN)

Compare $|-6|$ and $|-4|$. Use $>$, $<$, or $=$.

Practice

Building Skills

Write the absolute value for each integer.

1. $|-17|$ _____ **2.** $|-5|$ _____

3. $|-25|$ _____ **4.** $|-12|$ _____

5. $|-37|$ _____ **6.** $|-10|$ _____

Compare each pair of integers. Write $<$, $=$, or $>$ use.

7. $|15|$ $|-16|$ _____ **8.** $|8|$ $|-8|$ _____

9. $-|4|$ $|24|$ _____ **10.** $|-9|$ $|2|$ _____

11. $-|-4|$ $|9|$ _____ **12.** $|12|$ $|-1|$ _____

Problem Solving

Use absolute values to describe these statements.

13. The kite quickly dropped about 15 feet as the winds changed.

14. On his first spin, Jared lost 3 points.

15. Miranda lost 30 minutes of travel time when she stopped for lunch.

16. At the outdoor concert, the temperature dropped 15°F before the first band started to play.

17. The Larsons are giving Lydia 3 sweaters for her birthday.

18. Circulation of the school newspaper has dropped by 75 students.

19. The quarterback lost 7 yards.

20. The clock gained 12 minutes every month.

LESSON 14 **Square Numbers**

A **square number** is the answer when you multiply a number by itself. You have to tile an 8 foot by 8 foot room with tiles that are 1 foot by 1 foot. How many tiles do you need?

You can multiply 8 times 8.
$8 \times 8 = 64$.

You can also use 8^2 to show that 8 is multiplied by itself.

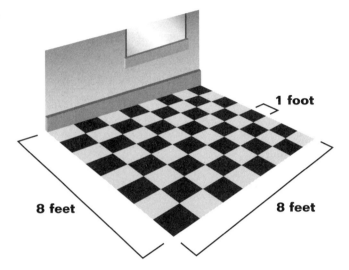

1 foot

8 feet   8 feet

Example

Evaluate. 5^2

STEP 1 Identify the factor and the exponent.
Factor is 5.   Exponent is 2.

STEP 2 Multiply the factor by itself.
The exponent tells you how many times the factor is multiplied.

$5 \times 5 = 25$

ON YOUR OWN

A poster for a music group shows 9 photos. There are 3 rows of concert photos, with 3 photos in each row. How can you express 9 using an exponent?

Practice

Building Skills

Find each square.

1. 5^2

2. 7^2

3. 10^2

4. 12^2

5. $(-5)^2$

6. $(-7)^2$

7. $(-8)^2$

8. $(-9)^2$

9. $(-10)^2$

10. $(-12)^2$

Problem Solving

Write each answer as a square number. Then solve.

11. A Russian checkerboard is 10 squares by 10 squares. How many squares are on the Russian checkerboard?

12. The school placed a special dance floor in the gym that measured 12 feet wide by 12 feet long. How many square feet of dance floor are there?

13. In a shop class, students built birdhouses for swallows. The birdhouse had 9 rows of holes with 9 holes in each row. How many holes are in the birdhouse?

14. Rajiv buys mini-pizzas at a discount store. Each package has 4 boxes. Each box has 4 mini-pizzas. How many pizzas are in a package?

15. Katrina spent 8 hours each week decorating her house for the past 8 weeks. How many hours did she decorate during this time?

16. There are 6 cans in a box. Each can has 6 ounces of green beans. How many ounces of green beans are in each box?

LESSON ⑮ Square Roots

Finding the square root of a number is the opposite of squaring a number.

The symbol for square root is $\sqrt{}$.

You have a square garden that is 25 square yards. What is the length of each side of the fence?

To solve this problem, you find the number multiplied by itself that equals 25.

25 is 5×5 or 5^2.

You can write $\sqrt{25} = 5$. You read this as *The **square root** of 25 equals 5.*

The length of each side of the fence for your garden is 5 yards.

| 25 sq yd. | ? |

Digit (n)	Square (n^2)
1	1
2	4
3	9
4	16
5	25
6	36
7	49
8	64
9	81
10	100
11	121
12	144

Example

Find $\sqrt{36}$.

STEP 1 Find a factor that when multiplied by itself equals the square number. Use the table to help you.

$6 \times 6 = 36$

STEP 2 Rewrite the problem and identify the square root of the number.

$\sqrt{36} = 6$

ON YOUR OWN

An art student has 81 square tiles to glue together. He wants to make one large square with these tiles. How many tiles will be on each side of the square?

Practice

Check your answer by multiplying.

Building Skills

Find each square root.

1. $\sqrt{49}$

2. $\sqrt{64} =$

3. $\sqrt{25} =$

4. $\sqrt{36} =$

5. $\sqrt{4} =$

6. $\sqrt{9} =$

7. $\sqrt{121} =$

8. $\sqrt{100} =$

9. $\sqrt{144} =$

Problem Solving

Solve each problem.

10. The school spirit club made a square pen for the school mascot. The area of the pen is 16 square feet. How long is each side?

11. There are 36 sandwiches arranged in equal rows on a square serving tray. How many sandwiches are in each row?

12. A game show has spaces for 25 letters arranged in a square. How many letters are on each side of the square?

13. The 49 members of the marching band formed a square as they lined up on the field. How many band members were in each row?

14. Ted used a 100-foot square section of his backyard to work on his motorcycle. What was the length of one side of this working space?

15. Lee used a square piece of fabric that was 144 square inches to make a section of a quilt. How long was each side of the piece of fabric?

Name _____ Date _____

LESSON 16   Cube Numbers

A square has two dimensions: length and width. You square a number to find the area in square units.

$4^2 = 4 \times 4 = 16$ square units

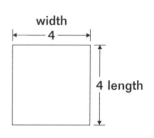

A **cube** has **three dimensions**: length, width, and height. The cube of a number uses a number as a factor three times.

$4^3 = 4 \times 4 \times 4 = 64$ cubic units

4^3 is read as **four cubed.**

Volume is measured in cubic units.

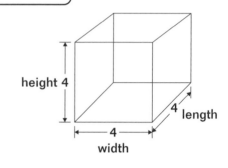

Example

Evaluate. 7^3

STEP 1 Identify the factor and the exponent.
Factor is 7.   Exponent is 3.

STEP 2 Multiply the factor 3 times.

$7^3 = 343$

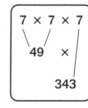

ON YOUR OWN

The Rubik's cube is a color-matching puzzle first made popular in the early 1980s. There are 3 colored squares along each side of a cube. On a giant Rubik's cube model in a toy museum, the side of each square is 1 foot. What is the volume of this model?

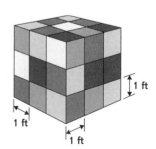

Practice

Building Skills

Solve.

1. 5^3

2. 10^3

3. 6^3

4. 9^3

5. 8^3

6. 7^3

7. 1^3

8. 11^3

9. 15^3

Problem Solving

Solve.

10. A packing box measures 10 inches on each side. How big is the box in cubic inches?

11. A gift box of oranges has 5 trays stacked on top of each other. Each tray has 5 rows of 5 oranges each. How many oranges are in a gift box?

12. A box of golf balls contains 6 balls. The boxes are laid out in 6 rows, with 6 boxes in each row. How many balls are in the display?

13. A container in the shape of a cube measures 15 inches on each side. How big is the box in cubic inches?

14. Fuzzy cubes that are 1 cubic foot each are stacked in a box that measures 3 feet on each side. How many cubes fit in the box?

15. You build a storage shed that measures 12 feet long, 12 feet tall, and 12 feet wide. How big is the shed in cubic feet?

LESSON **17** Operations with Exponents

Sometimes in math, different names are used to describe the same thing. For example, another name for exponent is power. The factor can be called the base.

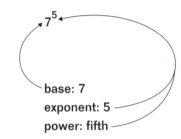

base: 7
exponent: 5
power: fifth

Remember: A number itself is considered to be the first power, or the power with exponent 1.

$$7^1 = 7$$

Read as: seven to the fifth power

When multiplying two powers with the same base, you just add the exponents.

$$7^2 \times 7^3 = 7^{2+3} = 7^5$$

Example

Multiply. $6^2 \times 6^3$

STEP 1 Identify the base.
6

STEP 2 Identify the exponents and add them.
$6^2 \times 6^3$: Exponents $2 + 3 = 5$, so $6^2 \times 6^3 = 6^5$

STEP 3 Rewrite the problem as a multiplication problem.
$6^5 = 6 \times 6 \times 6 \times 6 \times 6$

STEP 4 Multiply.
$6 \times 6 \times 6 \times 6 \times 6 = 7{,}776$

$6^2 \times 6^3 = 7{,}776$

(ON YOUR OWN)

Multiply $5^2 \times 5^4$.

Practice

Building Skills

Solve.

1. 5^4

2. $10^2 \times 10^2 =$

3. $8^2 \times 8^1 =$

4. $12^3 \times 12^3 =$

5. $7^3 \times 7^2 =$

6. $2^2 \times 2^5 =$

7. $1^2 \times 1^3 =$

8. $9^4 \times 9^3 =$

9. $4^2 \times 4^2 =$

10. $3^5 \times 3^2 =$

Problem Solving

Multiply.

11. $3^3 \times 3^1 =$

12. $2^2 \times 2^3 =$

13. $4^3 \times 4^6 \times 4^2 =$

14. $6^2 \times 6^3 =$

15. $2^8 \times 2^4 =$

16. $5^5 \times 5^{-3} =$

LESSON ⓲ Order of Operations

Look at the expression $5^2 + 3 \times 9$.

What should you do first?

If you could choose any order to do the computations, you would get a different answer every time. There is a standard **order of operations** to follow when computing numbers. In this example, the correct way to order the operations is to find the square of 5, then to multiply 3 times 9, then to add the 2 answers.

Just remember this sentence—Please Excuse My Dear Aunt Sally—to remember the rules for order of operations:

Beginning from the left, do the calculations in parentheses (P) first, then do operations for exponents (E); then multiply (M) and divide (D); then add (A) and finally subtract (S).

$$
\begin{aligned}
& 28 - 5 + 3^2 \times 5 \\
=\ & 28 - 5 + 9 \times 5 \\
=\ & 28 - 5 + 45 \\
=\ & 23 + 45 \\
=\ & 68
\end{aligned}
$$

Example

Evaluate $(14 + 7) - 3 \times 2^2$.

STEP 1 Finish all operations in the parentheses (P) first and rewrite the expression.

$21 - 3 \times 2^2$

STEP 2 Solve for any exponents (E) *from left to right* and rewrite the expression.

$21 - 3 \times (2 \times 2) = 21 - 3 \times 4$

STEP 3 Multiply (M) or divide (D) *from left to right* and rewrite the expression.

$21 - (3 \times 4) = 21 - 12$

STEP 4 Add (A) or subtract (S) *from left to right* and write the answer.

$21 - 12 = 9$

(ON YOUR OWN)

Evaluate $(6 + 3) \times 2^3 - 3 \times 2$.

Practice

Building Skills

Evaluate each expression.

1. $28 - 5 + 3^2 \times 5$

2. $2^2 + (5 - 3) \times 3$

3. $2^2 + 5 - 3 \times 3$

4. $(5 + 9) \times 4 - 8$

5. $5 + 9 \times 4 - 8$

6. $12 - 5 \times 2^3 - 3$

7. $(12 - 5) \times (2^3 - 3)$

8. $36 - 4 - 4^2 + 5$

9. $(36 - 4) - (4^2 + 5)$

Problem Solving

Write an expression and solve.

10. Nancy bought three CDs at $15 each and two CD carrying cases for $12 each. Tax on these items is $4. What is the total cost of Nancy's purchase?

11. In the new auditorium, there are 4 floor sections and 3 balconies. Each floor section seats 80 people. Each balcony section seats 50 people. How many seats are in the new auditorium?

12. Keesha works at a gift-wrap store during vacation. The cost of wrapping a package is $5. Customers can choose to add a bow for $1 or a card for $2. Keesha wrapped 30 packages, including 25 with bows and 11 with cards. How much money did Keesha collect from customers?

13. The cost of an adult ticket for a play is $5. The cost of a student ticket is $3. A child ticket costs $1. On opening night 120 adults, 70 students, and 20 children attended the play. What is the total amount collected for ticket sales for opening night?

14. Each week a coach buys 3 cases of water and 5 cases of sports drinks for practice. Each case of water holds 4 six-packs of bottles. Each case of sports drinks holds 4 four-packs of bottles. How many bottles does the team manager buy each week?

15. Monte bought 3 breakfast bars at $3 each and two bottles of juice at $2 each. He paid for these items with a $20 bill. How much change should Monte receive?

Name _____ Date _____

LESSON ⑲ Decimal Place Value

Decimal place value is similar to whole number place value. Look at the place-value chart. Find the decimal point. Notice that as you move to the left of the decimal point, each place is 10 times *greater* than the place on its right. As you move to the right of the decimal point, each place is $\frac{1}{10}$ times *smaller* than the place on its left.

When reading a decimal, read the decimal point as *and*.

Example

Look at the number 9.75**6**. Identify the value of the underlined digit.

STEP 1 Write the number in the place-value chart below.
Write "9" in the ones column, ".7" in the tenths column, "5" in the hundredths column, and "6" in the thousandths column.

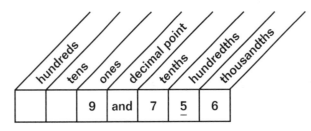

STEP 2 Write the name of the underlined digit and the name of its column.

5   hundredths

In the number 9.75**6**, the value of the underlined digit is 5 hundredths.

(**ON YOUR OWN**)

Look at the number 56.1**4**2. What is the value of the underlined digit?

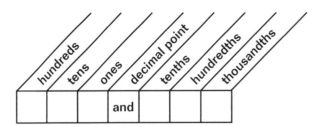

Practice

> The zeros to the right of a decimal point have a place value.

Building Skills

Solve each problem by finding the value of the underlined digit.

1. 10.978 _____

2. 67.004 _____

3. 0.31 _____

4. 987.265 _____

5. 74.27 _____

6. 9.859 _____

7. 32.153 _____

8. 12.098 _____

9. 52.435 _____

10. 61.74 _____

Problem Solving

For each problem, circle the correct answer.

11. Max is thinking of a 3-digit decimal. One of the digits is 8 tenths. Circle the number that he is thinking of.

5.893   5.98   8.67   6.87   4.998

12. Julie tried to memorize a secret 5-digit code. She forgot all but one digit, which is 9 thousandths. Circle the number shown below that might be the secret code.

42.503   9.1805   15.009   13.895   45.958

13. Yana won the 100-meter dash in 10.62 seconds. The second-place runner took 2 tenths seconds longer to finish. Circle the number that shows the second-place time.

8.62   10.42   10.82   10.24   9.62

14. Read the clues, then decide which 6-digit number is the mystery decimal and circle it.
- One of the digits is 7 tenths.
- The digit in the thousandths place is even.
- The digit in the hundredths place is twice the value of the digit in the thousandths place.

234.736   23.783   321.742   783.874   987.367

15. Last season Adrian had a batting average of 0.215. Angel had a higher batting average than Adrian. Circle the number that shows the higher batting average.

0.213   0.035   0.217   0.025   0.207

Name _____   Date _____

LESSON 20   Writing Decimals

When learning to write decimals, write the numbers in a place-value chart. Look at the chart and find the column farthest to the right with a number. The name of the decimal is taken from the name of that column. The name for the number in the chart is 298 thousandths. In standard form it is 0.298. The zero in the ones place tells you that the decimal is less than one.

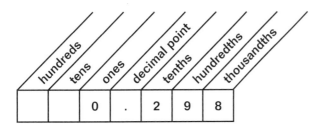

Example

Write 75 thousandths in standard form.

STEP 1 Look at the word after the number. This word tells where to put the last digit in the number.
The word *thousandths* tells you that the 5 will go into the thousandths column.

STEP 2 Write the decimal digits in the place-value chart to the right of the decimal point.
Write 5 in the thousandths column. Write 7 in the hundredths column.

STEP 3 If necessary, add zeros as placeholders to fill space between the decimal point and digits farther to the right.
Write 0 in the tenths place.

STEP 4 Write digits or 0 in the ones, tens, or hundreds place.
This decimal does not have whole numbers. Place "0" in the ones column.

75 thousandths in standard form is 0.075

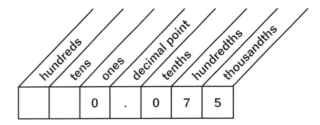

ON YOUR OWN

A bucket holds 12 and 85 hundredths gallons of water. Write the decimal in standard form.

Practice

> When you write a decimal, use a decimal point for *and*.

Building Skills

Write the decimal in standard form.

1. 1 and 465 thousandths _____

2. 12 and 79 thousandths _____

3. 48 hundredths _____

4. 2 and 7 tenths _____

5. 9 and 2 hundredths _____

6. 8 and 14 thousandths _____

7. 34 and 8 thousandths _____

8. 698 and 3 hundredths _____

9. 3 and 5 tenths _____

10. 325 and 26 hundredths _____

Problem Solving

For each problem, write the decimal in standard form.

11. Isabel is buying a sack of potatoes that weighs 5 and 2 hundredths of a pound.

_____

12. Ping runs the cross-country trail in her neighborhood every day. The trail is 2 and 4 tenths blocks long.

_____

13. In 1941, Ted Williams of the Boston Red Sox had a batting average of 406 thousandths.

_____

14. A marathon is 26 and 3 tenths miles long.

_____

15. An Internet search engine created the results of a search in 21 hundredths of a seconds.

_____

16. The average rainfall in January for Galveston, Texas, is 3 and 26 hundredths inches.

_____

17. A bottle of perfume contains 2 and 6 tenths ounces.

_____

18. A shoelace is about 31 and 3 tenths inches long.

_____

Name _____   Date _____

LESSON 21   Rounding and Estimating Decimals Using a Number Line

Rounding decimals is similar to rounding whole numbers. Suppose you want to round
1.13 to the nearest tenth. You can see that
1.13 is closer to 1.1 than to 1.2. So, 1.13
rounded to the nearest tenth is 1.1.

Look at the other numbers on the
number line.
All of the numbers less than 1.15 round down to 1.1.
The number 1.15 and everything greater round up to 1.2.

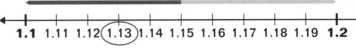

1.1 1.11 1.12 (1.13) 1.14 1.15 1.16 1.17 1.18 1.19 **1.2**

Example

Round 6.38 to the nearest tenth.

STEP 1 Find the digit in the place value you want to round to and circle it.

STEP 2 Underline the digit to the right of the circled digit.

STEP 3 If the underlined digit is 5 or greater, add 1 to the circled digit. If the underlined digit is less than 5, do not change the circled digit. Finally, drop the remaining digits to the right of the circled digit.

Because 8 is greater than 5, add 1 to the circled digit. Then drop the 8.

When rounded to the nearest tenth, 6.38 is 6.4.

ON YOUR OWN

Round 4.762 to the nearest hundredth.

Practice

Building Skills

> If the number to the right is 5 or >5, round up.

Solve each problem by rounding.

1. Round 34.671 to the nearest tenth.

_____

2. Round 8.36 to the nearest tenth.

_____

3. Round 143.62 to the nearest tenth.

_____

4. Round 9.256 to the nearest hundredth.

_____

5. Round 6.873 to the nearest hundredth.

_____

6. Round 0.723 to the nearest hundredth.

_____

7. Round 132.4521 to the nearest thousandth.

_____

8. Round 79.9901 to the nearest thousandth.

_____

Problem Solving

Use rounding to solve these problems.

9. Kanya rounds a decimal to the nearest tenth. Her answer is 34.9. Which decimal did she round up? Circle your answer.

34.09   34.87   34.96   34.99   34.00

10. Doli rounds a decimal to the nearest one (whole number). Her answer is 12. Which decimal could *not* have been the original decimal? Circle your answer.

12.41   11.987   12.378   11.47   12.2

11. The tadpole you measured in biology class is 3.65 inches long. How long is the tadpole to the nearest tenth of an inch?

12. Tanika's lunch cost $8.53 including the tip. She does not want to wait for change, so she decides to round the amount to the nearest dollar. How much money does Tanika leave?

LESSON 22 Comparing and Ordering Decimals

Look at the place value chart. When comparing decimals with different numbers of digits, you begin by adding zeros to the right of the last digit so that both decimals have the same number of digits.

Start with the whole numbers and then move right to the tenths, hundredths, and thousandths place. Stop when you find two digits in the same column that are different. In the example, there are two different digits in the thousandths place.

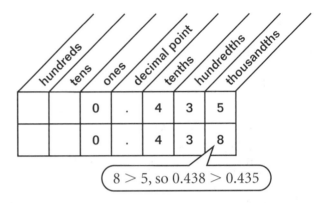

8 > 5, so 0.438 > 0.435

Example

Which decimal is greater, 0.78 or 0.781?

STEP 1 Find the number of digits in each decimal. If necessary, add zeros to the right of the last digit in the number with fewer digits until both decimals have the same number of digits.

0.78**0** (Add 1 zero)   0.781

STEP 2 Compare digits. Start on the left. When you find two different digits, underline them.

0.78<u>0</u>   0.78<u>1</u>

STEP 3 Compare the underlined digits. The decimal with the greater underlined digit is the greater number.

0.78<u>0</u>   0.78<u>1</u>
1 > 0, so 0.781 > 0.780.

0.781 > 0.78

ON YOUR OWN

Which decimal is greater, 6.405 or 6.45?

Practice

< less than
> greater than
= is equal to

Building Skills

Compare. Use <, >, or = sign.

1. 0.50 ☐ 0.5   **2.** 1.4 ☐ 1.45   **3.** 0.64 ☐ 0.69

4. 7.05 ☐ 7.50   **5.** 0.4 ☐ 0.400   **6.** 0.394 ☐ 0.394

Order the decimals from least to greatest.

7. 0.7   0.07   0.17   1.7   _____

8. 0.456   0.45   0.5   0.405   _____

Order the decimals from greatest to least.

9. 11.27   1.27   11.2   12.27   _____

10. 0.380   0.387   0.37   0.4   _____

Problem Solving

Use ordering to solve these problems.

11. A red pitcher holds 1.56 quarts of liquid and a green pitcher holds 1.5 quarts. Which pitcher holds the greater amount of liquid?

12. In 2002, 4.35 million people visited an amusement park. In 2003, 4.7 million people visited the park. Which year did the park have the greater number of visitors?

13. It costs $13.47 to run an air conditioner for one month. A clothes dryer costs $14.53 for electricity to run for one month and a refrigerator costs $14.65. Which appliance costs the most to use?

14. During June, it rained 0.20 inches in Tucson, Arizona. In San Diego, California, it rained 0.07 inches, and Anchorage, Alaska, had 1.14 inches of rainfall. Which city had the most rain in June?

Name _____   Date _____

LESSON **23**   **Adding Decimals**

You add decimals in the same way that you add whole numbers.

First, write the numbers so the decimal points line up. If there are empty spaces to the right of the last digit in any number, add zeros as placeholders.

Add. 1.539 + 0.53

hundreds	tens	ones	decimal point	tenths	hundredths	thousandths
		¹1	.	5	3	9
+		0	.	5	3	0
		2	.	0	6	9

Add a zero as a placeholder.

Next, put a decimal point in the answer directly below the other decimal points. Then add the same way you add whole numbers.

Example

Add. 3.45 + 0.638

STEP 1 Write the numbers so the decimal points line up.

3.45
+0.638

STEP 2 Add zeros as placeholders.

3.450
+0.638

STEP 3 Put a decimal point in the answer directly under the other decimal points.

STEP 4 Add. Regroup as necessary.

3.45 + 0.638 = 4.088

3.450
+0.638
4.088

ON YOUR OWN

Sam has two wooden boards. One board is 2.5 feet long. The other board is 3.56 feet long. If Sam glues the two boards together to make one long wooden board, how long will it be?

Lesson 23
Number Concepts, Decimals, and Graphs, SV 0435-2

Practice

Line up the decimal points before you add.

Building Skills

Add. Show your work.

1. 25.43 + 32.7 = _____

2. 1.598 + 12.4 = _____

3. 7 + 6.89 = _____

4. 3.015 + 7.96 = _____

5. 0.476 + 3.79 = _____

6. 4.109 + 0.47 = _____

7. 8.54 + 2.226 = _____

8. 3.17 + 8.036 = _____

9. 0.211 + 13.5 = _____

10. 56.7 + 12.25 = _____

Problem Solving

Add. Show your work.

11. Hoshi poured 2.7 quarts of water in a bucket. Then, she added 4.09 more quarts. How many quarts of water did Hoshi pour in the bucket?

12. In 2002, 4.5 million tourists visited Alcatraz prison, near San Francisco, California. The year before, 5.95 million visited. How many people visited Alcatraz in 2001 and 2002?

13. The decorator bought 13.4 yards of fabric to make curtains. He went back to the store and bought 6.98 more yards. How many yards of fabric did he buy in all?

14. The painter bought 15.57 gallons of red paint and 8 gallons of white paint. How many gallons of paint did she buy in all?

Name _____ Date _____

LESSON 24 Subtracting Decimals

You subtract decimals in the same way that you subtract whole numbers.

First, write the numbers so the decimal points line up. If there are empty spaces to the right of the last digit in any number, add zeros as placeholders.

Subtract. 6.792 − 0.57

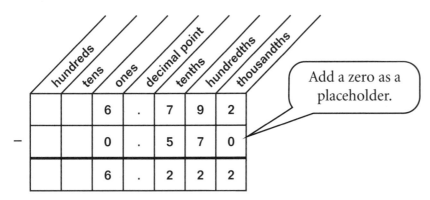

Add a zero as a placeholder.

Next, put a decimal point in the answer directly below the other decimal points. Then, subtract decimals the same way you subtract whole numbers.

Example

Subtract. 9.25 − 1.018

STEP 1 Write the numbers so the decimal points line up.

$$\begin{array}{r} 9.25 \\ -1.018 \end{array}$$

STEP 2 Add zeros as placeholders.

$$\begin{array}{r} 9.250 \\ -1.018 \end{array}$$

STEP 3 Place a decimal point in the answer directly under the other decimal points.

STEP 4 Subtract. Regroup as necessary.

9.25 − 1.018 = 8.232

$$\begin{array}{r} 9.2\overset{41}{5}0 \\ -1.018 \\ \hline 8.232 \end{array}$$

ON YOUR OWN

Asha had 29.5 quarts of syrup for ice drinks before the carnival started. She used 18.75 quarts. How many quarts of syrup did she have left?

Practice

> Line up the decimal points before you subtract.

Building Skills

Subtract. Show your work.

1. $14.93 - 2.74 =$ _____

2. $1.874 - 0.91 =$ _____

3. $7.51 - 6.215 =$ _____

4. $43.706 - 16.91 =$ _____

5. $0.879 - 0.68 =$ _____

6. $4.647 - 2.984 =$ _____

7. $6.23 - 3.985 =$ _____

8. $4.42 - 1.28 =$ _____

9. $0.806 - 0.54 =$ _____

10. $14.714 - 0.029 =$ _____

Problem Solving

Subtract. Show your work.

11. Students in the drama department were painting scenery for a play. They had 5.5 gallons of white paint and used 2.6 gallons to paint a winter scene. They need about 2.5 more gallons to finish. Will they have enough paint?

12. Coach Ortiz had 20.75 pints of sports drink for game night. The players drank 14.6 pints. How many pints were left over?

13. As a junior, Kira ran the 200-meter dash in 28.34 seconds. In her senior year, she ran it in 25.22 seconds. How many seconds faster was she in her senior year than in her junior year?

14. One day in August, the Dow Jones Industrial Average, a stock market index, ended the day at 10,179.16 points. On the next day, the index ended at 10,120.24. How many points lower did the index end on the second day?

Name _____   Date _____

LESSON 25 Multiplying Decimals by Whole Numbers

Suppose you drive 7.8 miles to and from school every weekday, and you want to find out how many miles you drive in a week. You can add 7.8 five times, but it is easier to multiply 7.8 and 5.

```
  4
  7.8
+ 7.8
+ 7.8                    4
+ 7.8                  7.8
+ 7.8                × 5
 39.0     OR          39.0
```

Example

Multiply. 28.3 × 6

STEP 1 Multiply.
Ignore the decimal point for now.

```
 4 1
 28.3
×   6
1698
```

STEP 2 Count the number of decimal places in each number.

```
28.3  ←— 1 decimal place
×  6  ←— 0 decimal places
1698  ←— 1 decimal place
```

STEP 3 Starting at the right side of the answer, count that number of decimal places to the left, and put the decimal point there.

28.3 × 6 = 169.8

```
 28.3  ←— 1 decimal place
×   6  ←— 0 decimal places
169.8  ←— 1 decimal place
```

ON YOUR OWN

Lorenzo is making 7 banners for the science fair. He needs 1.4 yards of fabric for each banner. How many yards of fabric does he need in all?

Practice

Remember to put the decimal point in your answer

Building Skills

Multiply. Show your work.

1. $9.9 \times 2 =$ _____

2. $7.2 \times 5 =$ _____

3. $4.13 \times 9 =$ _____

4. $61.7 \times 8 =$ _____

5. $0.45 \times 7 =$ _____

6. $27.4 \times 13 =$ _____

7. $1.32 \times 21 =$ _____

8. $12.5 \times 12 =$ _____

9. $60.1 \times 32 =$ _____

Problem Solving

Multiply. Show your work.

10. You are teaching crafts at a summer camp. Nine children want to make yarn dolls. If each doll takes 3.5 yards of yarn, how many yards will you need in all?

11. A popular model of car gets 34.5 miles per gallon. Its gas tank holds 14 gallons. How far could you go on a full tank of gas?

12. Three auto mechanics each work 8.5 hours a day. What is the total number of hours they work?

13. Rosario is responsible for ordering supplies for the Chinese restaurant. The 12 soy sauce containers hold 4.5 gallons each and need to be refilled every week. How many gallons of soy sauce should Rosario order?

Name _____ Date _____

Multiplying Decimals by Decimals

Suppose you want to buy wood to make a frame for a picture. The wood is $2.10 per foot and you need 4.5 feet. To find the total cost of the wood, you could add. However, it is easier and faster to multiply.

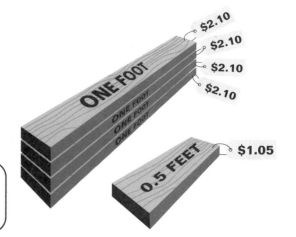

$2.10 + $2.10 + $2.10 + $2.10 + $1.05 = $9.45

or

$2.10 × 4.5 = $9.45

Four 1-foot pieces at $2.10 each; 1 half-foot piece at $1.05.

Example

Multiply. 5.3 × 2.8

STEP 1 Multiply.
Ignore the decimal point for now.

```
  5.3
 ×2.8
  424
 106
 1484
```

STEP 2 Count the number of decimal places in each number.

```
  5.3  ←— 1 decimal place
 ×2.8  ←— 1 decimal place
  424
 106
 1484 ←— 2 decimal places
```

STEP 3 Starting at the right side of the answer, count that number of places to the left and put the decimal point there.

5.3 × 2.8 = 14.84

```
14.84 ←— 2 decimal places
```

ON YOUR OWN

Rose is making a poster for her science exhibit. It is 2.4 feet long by 1.8 feet wide. What is the area of the poster? *(Area = length × width)*

Name _____ Date _____

Practice

Count the number of decimal places.

Building Skills

Multiply. Show your work.

1. $4.2 \times 1.3 =$ _____

2. $4.9 \times 0.2 =$ _____

3. $5.03 \times 6.8 =$ _____

4. $8.7 \times 0.13 =$ _____

5. $8.1 \times 0.22 =$ _____

6. $24.1 \times 0.14 =$ _____

7. $1.32 \times 2.4 =$ _____

8. $13.9 \times 2.7 =$ _____

9. $4.8 \times 3.8 =$ _____

Problem Solving

Multiply to solve each problem. Show your work.

10. The weight of a calf increases 4.3 pounds a day. How much weight will a calf gain in 7.5 days?

11. Pistachios cost $4.80 a pound. How much will 3.25 pounds cost?

12. Devon gets paid $9.30 an hour. If he works 25.6 hours, how much will he get paid?

13. Lily is making a travel crate for her dog. The bottom can be no more than 22 square feet. One side is 4.2 feet and the other side is 5.1 feet. To find the area, multiply 4.2 and 5.1. Is the area greater than 22 square feet?

LESSON 27 Dividing Decimals by Whole Numbers

You use division when you want to separate an amount into equal parts. Suppose you have $13.75 to spend on school lunches for a week. How much can you spend each day?

To find out, divide $13.75 by 5. You have to remember to put the decimal point in the quotient directly above the decimal point in the dividend. You can spend $2.75 a day for lunch.

quotient
$$5\overline{)13.75} \quad 2.75$$
divisor   dividend

Example

Divide. $25.13 \div 7$

STEP 1 Divide.
You can ignore the decimal point for now.

$$\begin{array}{r} 3\,59 \\ 7\overline{)25.13} \\ \underline{21} \\ 4\,1 \\ \underline{3\,5} \\ 63 \\ \underline{63} \\ 0 \end{array}$$

STEP 2 Look at the decimal point in the dividend. Put a decimal point directly above it in the answer.

STEP 3 If the decimal point falls to the left of the first digit in the quotient, place a zero in the ones place. (This step is not needed here.)

$$25.13 \div 7 = 3.59$$

$$\begin{array}{r} 3.59 \\ 7\overline{)25.13} \\ \underline{21} \\ 4\,1 \\ \underline{3\,5} \\ 63 \\ \underline{63} \\ 0 \end{array}$$

ON YOUR OWN

An art teacher has 3.5 yards of fabric. She divides it among seven students for a project. How much fabric does each student get?

Practice

Building Skills

Divide. Show your work.

1. $19.8 \div 2 =$ _____

2. $7.2 \div 5 =$ _____

3. $37.17 \div 9 =$ _____

4. $493.6 \div 8 =$ _____

5. $3.15 \div 7 =$ _____

6. $356.2 \div 13 =$ _____

7. $27.72 \div 21 =$ _____

8. $150.6 \div 12 =$ _____

9. $195.2 \div 32 =$ _____

Problem Solving

Divide. Show your work.

10. Kaleesha went on a surfing trip with friends. She had $150.00. If she was gone for 4 days, how much money could she spend each day?

11. Andrew uses 52.5 cups of flour to make oatmeal cookies for a bake sale. If he makes 15 batches of cookies, how many cups of flour does he use for each batch?

12. Natasha earns $163.90 a week working at a health club juice bar. She works 22 hours in a week. How much is she paid per hour?

13. A package of string cheese contains 16.875 ounces of cheese. If there are 15 pieces of cheese in the package, how many ounces does each piece weigh?

LESSON **28** Dividing Decimals by Decimals

Dividing a decimal by a decimal is similar to dividing decimals by whole numbers. Now you will have to change the divisor to a whole number before you begin dividing.

Example

Birdseed costs $1.21 for 2.75 pounds. How much does 1 pound cost? Divide. $1.21 ÷ 2.75

STEP 1 Set up the problem.

divisor
$2.75\overline{)1.21}$
dividend

STEP 2 Count the number of decimal places in the divisor.
Each decimal has two decimal places to the right of the decimal point.

$2.75\overline{)1.21}$
2 decimal places ⤒⤒   ⤒⤒ 2 decimal places

STEP 3 Move the decimal points as many places as there are decimal places in the divisor.
Move the decimal point two places to the right.

$2.75\overline{)1.21}$

STEP 4 Divide. Add zeros as necessary.

```
       0 44
275.)121.00
     110 0
      11 00
      11 00
          0
```

STEP 5 Put a decimal point in your answer directly above the dividend. If the decimal point falls to the left of the first digit in the quotient, place a zero to the left of the decimal point.

The birdseed is $0.44 per pound.

```
       0.44
275.)121.00
     110 0
      11 00
      11 00
          0
```

ON YOUR OWN

Manuel bought 4.6 pounds of fresh fish for $14.03. How much did the fish cost per pound?

Practice

Move the decimal point to the right the same number of places in the divisor and dividend.

Building Skills

Divide. Show your work.

1. $367.2 \div 7.2 =$ _____

2. $0.48 \div 2.4 =$ _____

3. $9.8 \div 4.9 =$ _____

4. $61.5 \div 12.3 =$ _____

5. $9.72 \div 7.2 =$ _____

6. $356.2 \div 1.3 =$ _____

7. $2.100 \div 0.56 =$ _____

8. $8.4 \div 0.42 =$ _____

9. $5.856 \div 0.32 =$ _____

Problem Solving

Divide. Show your work.

10. A sandwich shop buys smoked cheese for $3.25 per pound. The shop spent $48.75 for cheese. How many pounds of cheese did the shop buy?

11. Josh wants to make new covers for several chairs. He has 34.5 yards of fabric and needs to use 5.75 yards for each chair. How many chairs can he cover?

Name _____ Date _____

LESSON 29 Changing Fractions to Decimals and Decimals to Fractions

In 2001, 7 out of 10 high-school students were able to graduate. You can write this relationship as $\frac{7}{10}$. You can also express $\frac{7}{10}$ as a decimal, 0.7. Changing decimals to fractions and fractions to decimals is easy once you learn the simple rules.

Example

Change $\frac{4}{5}$ to a decimal.

STEP 1 Find an equivalent fraction with a denominator of 10 or 100. To find an equivalent fraction, you must multiply the numerator and denominator by the same number.

$$\frac{4}{5} \times \frac{2}{2} = \frac{8}{10}$$

STEP 2 Write the name of the equivalent fraction. Then write the decimal.

The fraction $\frac{4}{5}$ can be written as the decimal 0.8.

$\frac{8}{10}$ ⟶ eight tenths ⟶ 0.8

Example

Change 0.52 to a fraction.

STEP 1 Write the word name for the decimal. The word name for 0.52 is fifty-two hundredths.

STEP 2 Write the word name as a fraction.

STEP 3 Simplify if possible.

0.52 can be written as the fraction $\frac{13}{25}$.

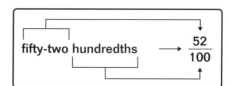

fifty-two hundredths ⟶ $\frac{52}{100}$

$$\frac{52}{100} = \frac{13}{25}$$

(ON YOUR OWN)

Six out of 50 people are left-handed. Write the fraction $\frac{6}{50}$ as a decimal.

The world's smallest fish, the stout infantfish, is 0.28 inches long. Write the decimal 0.28 as a fraction.

Practice

Reduce all fractions to lowest terms.

Building Skills

Write each fraction as a decimal. Show your work.

1. $\frac{1}{5}$ _____

2. $\frac{3}{4}$ _____

3. $\frac{31}{50}$ _____

4. $\frac{7}{25}$ _____

5. $\frac{9}{10}$ _____

6. $\frac{7}{8}$ _____

Write each decimal as a fraction.

7. 0.08 _____

8. 0.23 _____

9. 0.03 _____

10. 0.6 _____

11. 0.4 _____

12. 0.75 _____

Problem Solving

Change between fractions and decimals. Show your work.

13. Ken Marimoto got $\frac{6}{25}$ of the votes in the election for mayor. Write this fraction as a decimal.

14. A survey showed that $\frac{7}{20}$ of adults never heard a hip-hop performance. Write this fraction as a decimal.

15. A report stated that 0.55 of the people in the U.S. have used the Internet. Write the decimal as a fraction.

16. One serving of chicken noodle soup gives you 0.04% of the vitamin A you need every day. Write the decimal as a fraction.

Name _____ Date _____

A **line graph** is used to show continuous changes in data. For example, from the time you were born you grew taller each day, not just on your birthday. A line graph illustrates this continuous growth.

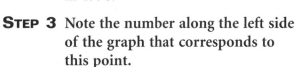

Look at the Theme Park line graph.

How many people attended theme parks in 1996?

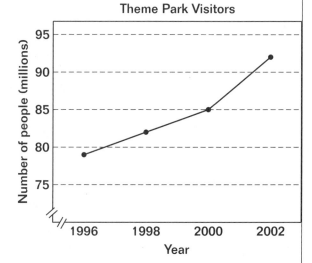

Theme Park Visitors

STEP 1 Find the area of data that you need along the bottom of the graph.
In this example, find the year 1996.

STEP 2 Move to a point above the place that you found in Step 1.
This point represents the number of people who went to the theme park in 1996.

STEP 3 Note the number along the left side of the graph that corresponds to this point.
The number 79 corresponds to the point above 1996.
The label on the left side of the graph tells you that this number represents 79 million people. That means that 79 million people attended the theme park in 1996.

Do you see a pattern in the theme park graph?

STEP 1 Notice the value of each point that matches several data items.
79 million people in 1996, 82 million in 1998, and 85 million in 2000

STEP 2 Describe any pattern that you notice.
Attendance at the theme park continues to grow each year.

(**ON YOUR OWN**)

How many people attended theme parks in 2002?
What is the attendance pattern from 1996–2000?

Practice

Building Skills

Use the line graph to answer questions 1–9.

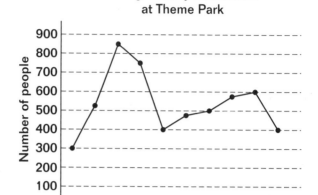

Average Hourly Attendance at Theme Park

1. What is the average theme park attendance at 10 A.M.?

   _____

2. What is the average attendance at 2 P.M.?

   _____

3. At what time of day is the attendance the same as at 2 P.M.?

   _____

4. In which hour of the day is attendance the highest?

   _____

5. During which hour of the day is attendance the lowest?

   _____

6. At what time of day does attendance begin to decrease?

   _____

7. At what time in the afternoon does attendance begin to increase?

   _____

8. Between which two hours does attendance increase the most?

   _____

9. In which hour is attendance twice as much as it is in the first hour the park is open?

   _____

Problem Solving

Use the line graph above to answer questions 10–13.

10. How much does attendance increase between 10 A.M. and noon?

11. How much does attendance decrease between 1 o'clock and 2 o'clock?

12. About how many people leave the park from noon to 2 P.M.?

13. What is the range in data on the Theme Park Graph? Remember: range is from least to greatest.

LESSON 31 Double Line Graphs

Double line graphs show how two sets of data change over time. The double line graph shows how much money teenagers normally spend on clothes each season.

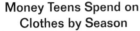

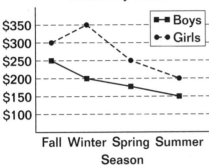

Money Teens Spend on
Clothes by Season

■━■ Boys
●╍● Girls

$350
$300
$250
$200
$150
$100

Fall Winter Spring Summer
Season

Example

According to the double line graph, who spends more money on clothes in the fall, teenage boys or girls?

STEP 1 Find the area of data that you need along the bottom of the graph.
Find *Fall* at the bottom of the graph.

STEP 2 Go to the points on the lines above the place you found in STEP 1.
The point on each line shows spending in the fall.

STEP 3 Look to the left side of the graph to find the data for each point.
The left side of the graph tells you the number amount, in dollars, that the point represents.
Girls, $300   Boys, $250

STEP 4 Compare the data.
$300 > $250

Girls spend more money on clothes in the fall than boys do.

ON YOUR OWN

How do girls' spending habits change each season?

Name _____ Date _____

Practice

Building Skills

Use the double line graph to answer questions 1–9.

1. During which year was attendance at the prom the highest?

   _____

2. About how many students attended that year?

   _____

3. During which year was attendance at the homecoming dance the highest?

   _____

Students Attending the Homecoming Dance and Prom

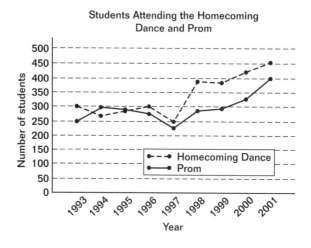

4. About how many students attended that year?

   _____

5. In which year was attendance the same for both events?

   _____

6. In which year was attendance at the prom higher than at the homecoming dance?

   _____

7. In which year was there the biggest difference in attendance at these school events?

   _____

8. In which two years in a row was attendance at each event about the same?

   _____

9. In which year was attendance at both events down from the year before?

   _____

Problem Solving

Use the double line graph above to answer questions 10–13.

10. About how many more students attended the homecoming dance than the prom in 1993?

11. Estimate the change in attendance at the homecoming dance from 1998 to 2001.

12. Estimate the change in attendance at the prom between 1993 and 2001.

13. About how much did attendance decrease at the homecoming dance between 1997 and 1998?

Name _____   Date _____

LESSON 32   Bar Graphs

A **bar graph** shows countable data. Horizontal or vertical bars can be used to represent the data. The length of each bar stands for a number.

Example

Look at the Top-Selling Albums graph.

How do *Born in the U.S.A.* sales compare with Mariah Carey's *Daydream* album sales?

STEP 1 Find the areas of data needed along the bottom of the graph.
Look for the album titles *Born in the U.S.A.* and *Daydream.*

STEP 2 Look at the length of the bars for each data item. Find the number at the left side of the graph that represents each length.
Born in the U.S.A. sold 15 million albums.
Daydream sold 10 million albums.

STEP 3 Compare the data.
15 million − 10 million = 5 million

***Born in the U.S.A.* sold 5 million more albums than *Daydream*.**

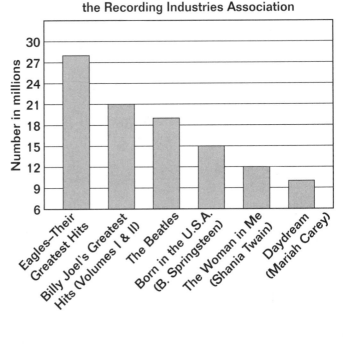

All-Time Top-Selling Albums from the Recording Industries Association

(ON YOUR OWN)

How does *The Beatles* album sales compare with the top-selling album?
(Hint: Top-selling album is the longest bar.)

Name _____   Date _____

Practice

Building Skills

Use the bar graph to answer questions 1–9.

1. How many 2-door coupes were sold during this 6-month period?

_____

2. How many sports cars were sold during this time period?

_____

3. Which type of vehicle had the most sales?

_____

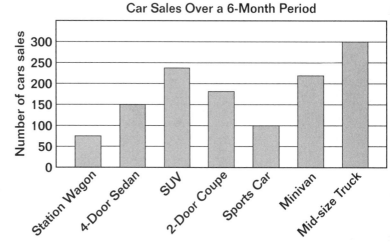

Car Sales Over a 6-Month Period

4. Which type of car had the fewest sales?

_____

5. Which vehicle sales were almost double sports car sales?

_____

6. Which vehicle sales were half as much as mid-size truck sales?

_____

7. Which vehicles had more than 200 sales?

_____

8. Which vehicles had fewer than 150 sales?

_____

9. Which vehicle had the second-highest sales?

_____

Problem Solving

Use the bar graph above to answer questions 10–13.

10. How many more sedans than station wagons were sold?

11. Estimate the total number of minivans and station wagons sold.

12. What is the difference between mid-size truck sales and sports car sales?

13. What are the combined sales of 4-door sedans and 2-door coupes?

LESSON ③③ Double Bar Graphs

Double bar graphs show two sets of data and allow you to compare them. The double bar graph shows how 100 teenage boys and 100 teenage girls usually spend their time in the evening.

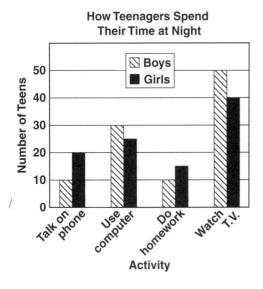

How Teenagers Spend Their Time at Night

Number of Teens (y-axis): 0, 10, 20, 30, 40, 50

Legend: ▨ Boys ■ Girls

Activity (x-axis): Talk on phone, Use computer, Do homework, Watch T.V.

Activity

Example

Do more teenage boys or more teenage girls spend time on homework?

STEP 1 Find the area of data needed along the bottom of the bar graph.
In this example, find *Do homework*.

STEP 2 Compare the two bars that match the data area.
The teenage girls' bar is higher, so more teenage girls spend time on homework.

Which activity did teenage girls choose twice as often as teenage boys?

STEP 1 Look for data bars that match the requirements.
One bar must be twice as long as another.
20 is twice 10.

STEP 2 Look at the label along the bottom of the graph that identifies these two bars.

Teenage girls chose talking on the phone twice as often as teenage boys did.

(ON YOUR OWN)

Which activity was chosen most by the teenagers?

How did their choice of *Use computer* compare?

Lesson 33
Number Concepts, Decimals, and Graphs, SV 0435-2

Practice

Building Skills

Use the double bar graph to answer questions 1–7.

1. Which class has sold more popcorn tins?

_____

2. About how much money has the sophomore class raised selling popcorn?

_____

3. Which item has the junior class sold the fewest of?

_____

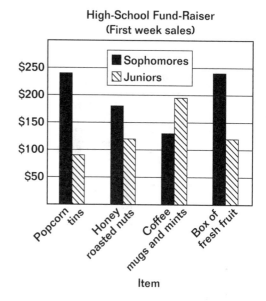

High-School Fund-Raiser
(First week sales)

Item

4. About how much money has the junior class raised selling popcorn?

_____

5. With which two items have the sophomores raised the same amount of money?

_____

6. Which item have the juniors sold more of than the sophomores?

_____

7. Which item have the sophomores sold about twice as much of as the juniors?

_____

Problem Solving

Use the double bar graph above to answer questions 8–11.

8. Estimate popcorn-tin sales for both classes during the first week of the fund-raiser.

9. About how much more money did the sophomore class raise in popcorn-tin sales than the junior class?

10. If the sophomore class continues to sell boxes of fresh fruit at the same rate for four weeks, about how much money will they raise?

11. If the junior class continues to sell coffee mugs and mints at the same rate for two more weeks, about how much money will they raise?

LESSON 34   Circle Graphs

A **circle graph** shows how parts of the data are related to the whole and to each other. Circle graphs use fractions or percents to compare the data. In a circle graph, the whole equals 100% or 1. Look at the circle graph. It shows traits that teenagers might use to describe themselves.

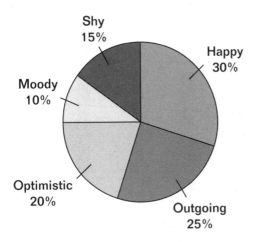

Shy 15%
Happy 30%
Moody 10%
Optimistic 20%
Outgoing 25%

Example

If 500 teenagers were surveyed, how many teenagers described themselves as *optimistic*?

STEP 1 Find the section of the circle graph that identifies the area of data needed.
In this example, look for the *Optimistic* section.
20% of the teenagers surveyed chose optimistic.

STEP 2 Write an expression for the problem asked.
20% of 500

STEP 3 Change the percent to a fraction or decimal, then solve.

$\frac{1}{5}$ of 500 = 100   or   0.20 × 500 = 100

100 teenagers described themselves as *optimistic*.

ON YOUR OWN

How many of the 500 teenagers described themselves as *outgoing?*

Practice

Building Skills

Use the circle graph to answer questions 1–8.

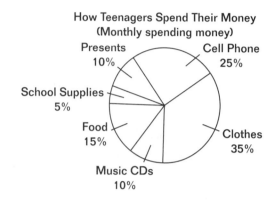

How Teenagers Spend Their Money
(Monthly spending money)

Presents 10%
Cell Phone 25%
School Supplies 5%
Food 15%
Clothes 35%
Music CDs 10%

1. What percent of a teenager's spending money is spent on clothes?

_____

2. What percent of their money do teenagers spend on food?

_____

3. What percent of a teen's spending money is spent on presents?

_____

4. Teenagers spend the same amount of money on which two items?

_____

5. Which item do teens spend the most money on?

_____

6. Which item do teens spend the least amount of money on?

_____

7. Which two items make up half (50%) of a teen's spending money?

_____

8. Which three items make up 25% of teen's spending money?

_____

Problem Solving

Use the circle graph above to answer questions 9–12.

9. Suppose Janna has $60 per month for spending money. How much money would she spend on food?

10. How much money would Janna spend on clothes?

11. How much money would Janna spend on her cell phone?

12. Mark has twice as much spending money each month as Janna. How much money would Mark spend on music CDs in one month?

LESSON 35 Venn Diagrams

A **Venn diagram** is a drawing that shows how different sets of objects are related to each other. Look at the Venn diagram of School Events.

Notice that:
• Each of the 3 circles stands for one teenager: Anna, Tina, and Lisa.
• All 3 circles overlap in the center to show that all 3 teenagers have something in common: All 3 teenagers are girls.

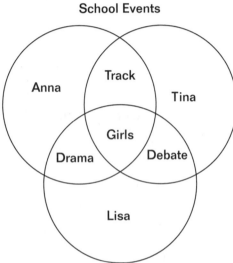

School Events

Example

What school event do Tina and Lisa have in common that Anna does not?

STEP 1 Trace around the area that represents each set of needed data.
Trace Tina's circle. Trace Lisa's circle.

STEP 2 Find where the circles overlap. Identify any common items.
Debate

STEP 3 Write a statement to describe this relationship

Tina and Lisa both take Debate, but Anna does not.

ON YOUR OWN

What school event do Anna and Lisa have in common that Tina does not?

Practice

Building Skills

Use the Venn diagram to answer questions 1–8.

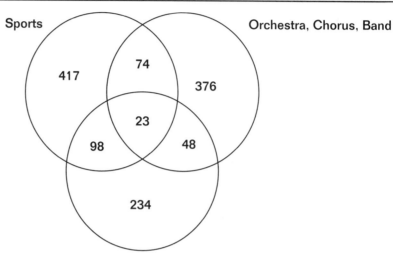

1. What school activities do each of the three circles in the Venn diagram represent?

   _____

2. How many high-school students had *only* Orchestra, Chorus, Band as their activity?

   _____

3. How many students *only* played Sports?

   _____

4. How many students participated *only* in Speech, Debate, Drama?

   _____

5. How many students took Orchestra, Chorus, Band *and* Sports?

   _____

6. How many students took Speech, Debate, Drama *and* Sports?

   _____

7. How many students took Speech, Debate, Drama *and* Orchestra, Chorus, Band?

   _____

8. How many students were in all 3 activities?

   _____

Problem Solving

Use the Venn diagram above to answer questions 9–12.

9. How many students were in Sports?

10. How many students were in Orchestra, Chorus, Band?

11. How many students were in Speech, Debate, Drama?

12. How many students chose to be in two activities?

LESSON 36 Frequency Tables and Line Plots

The **frequency table** lists each basketball player and the points he made during a weekend tournament. The **line plot,** an easy way to organize data on a number line, displays an X on the number line for each player's points.

Player	Number of points
Mark	4
Alberto	4
Kang	6
Tim	13
Michael	6
Hakeem	9
Kasem	8
Joe	5
Jamil	8
Stephen	2

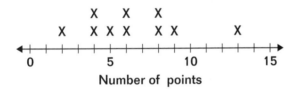

Number of points

Example

How many players scored 5 points or fewer during the tournament?

STEP 1 Identify the number in question on the line plot.
Identify 5 on the line plot.

STEP 2 Count the number of Xs.
There are 4 Xs on the line plot that represent 5 or fewer.

STEP 3 Write your answer.

Four players scored 5 or fewer points.

ON YOUR OWN

How many players scored between 5 and 10 points?

Practice

Building Skills

Use the frequency table and line plot to answer questions 1–6.

1. How many 15-year-olds are in the club?

_____

2. Which age level has the least number of members?

_____

3. Which age levels have the same number of members?

_____

Service Club	
Age	Number of members
14	1
15	3
16	4
17	5
18	5
19	2

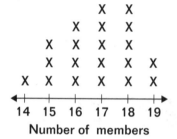

4. Large spaces between data values on a line plot are called gaps. Do you see any gaps in the members' ages? Explain.

_____

5. How old is the youngest member in the club?

_____

6. How old is the oldest member in the club?

_____

Problem Solving

Use the frequency table and line plot above to answer questions 7–12.

7. How many more 18-year-olds than 19-year-olds are in the club?

8. How many service club members are younger than 17?

9. How many members are older than 16?

10. How many members are in the club?

11. What is the difference in age between the oldest and youngest member in the club?

12. How do the members' ages in this club compare to the members' ages in a club at your school? Explain.

LESSON 37   Scatter Plots

A **scatter plot** is a graph of ordered pairs of numbers that show events. If both numbers in the ordered pairs tend to increase, then there is a *positive relationship* between events. If one number in each ordered pair tends to increase while the other number tends to decrease, then there is a *negative relationship* between events.

Study the scatter plot Driver's Test Scores. A score of 60 or more is needed to pass the test.

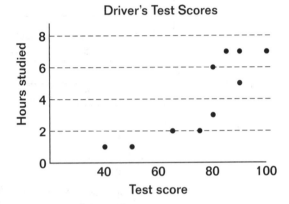

Example

Do teens who study less than two hours pass or fail the test?

STEP 1 Identify the ordered pairs.
In this example, look at one hour of study.
(1, 40), (1, 50)

STEP 2 Describe what the ordered pairs represent.
One hour of study results in a test score of 40 or 50.

Is the relationship between the events in the whole scatter plot positive or negative?

STEP 1 Describe the relationship between the ordered pairs.
One hour of study results in failing test scores.

STEP 2 Determine if the relationship between the ordered pairs is positive or negative.
Since low test scores result from small amounts of study time and high test scores come from high amounts of study time, the relationship is positive.

(ON YOUR OWN)

Do teens who study more than two hours pass or fail the test?

Is the relationship between these events positive or negative?

Name _____ Date _____

Practice

Building Skills

Use the scatter plot to answer questions 1–6.

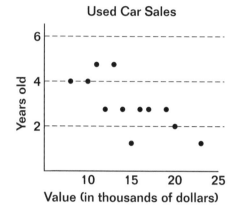

Used Car Sales

1. What do the values along the *y*-axis of the scatter plot stand for?

   _____

2. What do the values along the *x*-axis of the scatter plot represent?

   _____

3. Estimate the lowest price for a 3-year-old car shown on the scatter plot.

   _____

4. Estimate the highest price for a 3-year-old car shown on the scatter plot.

   _____

5. How many 5-year-old cars are shown on the scatter plot?

   _____

6. Which car age is shown least on the scatter plot?

   _____

Problem Solving

Use the scatter plot above to answer questions 7–12.

7. How many cars that are 3 years old or older are shown on the scatter plot?

8. If the 4-year-old cars were sold, would a car dealer have more or less than $20,000? Explain.

9. Is this statement true or false? *The older the car, the more it costs.*

10. Is this statement true or false? *The newer the car, the more it costs.*

11. Does the scatter plot show a positive or negative relationship? Explain.

12. Estimate the value of a 6-year-old car. Explain.

Number Concepts, Decimals, and Graphs, SV 0435-2

LESSON 38 Stem-and-Leaf Plots

A **stem-and-leaf plot** is a way to organize data to show how they are spread around. The data may be clustered or grouped together. The stem identifies the leading digit or digits in a number. The leaf identifies the digit in the ones place in a number.

Study the stem-and-leaf plot of teenage drivers' scores on a practice test. Notice that scores in the 20s, 30s, and 40s are grouped together.

Scores on Practice Test

Stem	Leaves
0	9
1	5 8
2	0 3 4 7 8
3	0 1 3 4 5 5 6 7 8 8 8 9
4	0 0 1 1 2 3 4 6 7 9
5	0

Legend: 3 | 4 means 34 correct answers on driver's written practice test.

Example

A test score of 35 or above is passing. How many teens passed the driving test?

STEP 1 Identify the stem and leaf for the number in question.
For the number 35, the stem is 3 and the leaf is 5.

STEP 2 Count how many times that number appears on the plot, and count how many numbers are higher than that number.
There are 8 students who scored 35–39.
There are 10 students who scored 40–49.
One student had a perfect score of 50.

STEP 3 Add the numbers to answer the question.
10 + 8 + 1 = 19

Nineteen teens passed the test.

ON YOUR OWN

If a teen scores less than 35, he or she does not pass the test.
How many teens did not pass the test?

84

Practice

Building Skills

Use the stem-and-leaf plot to answer questions 1–7.

Number of Cans of Food Collected Each Day

Stem	Leaves
0	8
1	2
2	3
3	5
4	8 9
5	6 8
6	3 8
7	0 1 1 3 4 9
8	
9	1 8 9
10	1 3

Legend: 4 | 8 means 48 cans of food were collected in one day.

1. The stem-and-leaf plot shows the number of cans of food collected each day. How many days did the math class collect food?

_____

2. How many days did the math class collect fewer than 20 cans of food?

_____

3. Did the math class collect 80–89 cans on any of the days? Explain.

_____

4. Were there any days that the math class collected the same number of cans? Explain how you know.

_____

5. How many days did the math class collect more than 100 cans?

_____

6. For how many days did the class collect fewer than 50 cans?

_____

7. How many days did the class collect from 70 to 79 cans?

_____

Problem Solving

Use the stem-and-leaf plot to answer questions 8–13.

8. On the days that students brought in 35 or fewer cans, how many cans were collected?

9. On the days that students brought in 50 to 70 cans, how many cans were collected?

10. On the days that students brought in more than 90 cans, how many cans were collected?

11. On the days students brought in 70 to 80 cans, how many cans were collected?

12. Do you think the class collected more than 1,000 cans of food? Explain how you know.

13. Are any of the number of cans collected grouped or clustered together? Explain.

LESSON 39   Histograms

A **histogram** looks very much like a bar graph. The only difference is that the bars represent the number of times data occur within certain *intervals* or periods. This histogram shows the number of minutes teens spend on the Internet answering e-mail messages.

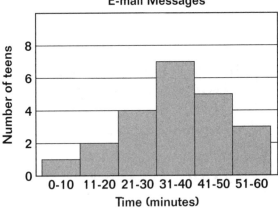

Example

How many teens spend more than 40 minutes answering messages?

STEP 1   Identify the intervals.
The interval must be more than 40 minutes.
The intervals are 41–50 minutes and 51–60 minutes.

STEP 2   Determine the number represented for each interval.
Five teens spend 41–50 minutes.
Three teens spend 51–60 minutes.

STEP 3   Add the numbers to answer the question.
3 + 5 = 8

Therefore, 8 teens spend more than 40 minutes answering e-mail messages.

ON YOUR OWN

How many teens spend 30 minutes or less answering e-mail messages?

Practice

Building Skills

Use the histogram to answer questions 1–7.

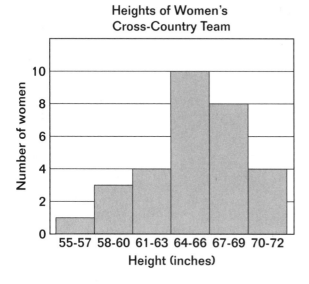

Heights of Women's
Cross-Country Team

1. Which interval on the histogram represents the shortest women's heights?

_____

2. Which interval represents the tallest women's heights?

_____

3. How many women are 70–72 in. tall?

_____

4. Which height intervals have the same number of women in them?

_____

5. How many women are shown in each of these equal intervals?

_____

6. Which height interval has twice as many women as the 70–72 in. interval?

_____

7. What intervals do most of the women's heights cluster around?

_____

Problem Solving

Use the histogram above to answer questions 8–13.

8. How many women on the team are at least 64 in. tall?

9. How many women are shorter than 64 in.?

10. How many women are on the cross-country team?

11. How many women are taller than 5 ft?

12. What is the shortest height in feet and inches?

13. Would you say that more than half of the women on the cross-country team are taller than 5 ft 3 in.? Explain.

LESSON 40 Surveys

When trying to decide which movie to see, you ask your friends which movies they have seen and liked. As you gather this data, you are making an informal poll, or **survey,** to help you make a good decision.

This frequency table shows the results of a teen survey about the number of movies watched each month.

Number of Movies Teens Watch Per Month

Number of Movies	Tally	Frequency
0		
1	II	2
2	IIII	4
3	IIII III	8
4	IIII	4
5	III	3
6	III	3

Example

What percent of the teens surveyed chose the answer that appeared most often?

STEP 1 Identify the graph item being questioned.
Here the question asks for the answer that appeared most often— 3 movies.

STEP 2 Find how often this item was chosen.
There were 8 teens who chose the answer *3 movies.*

STEP 3 Identify the total number surveyed.
$2 + 4 + 8 + 4 + 3 + 3 = 24$ teens

STEP 4 Write the ratio and percent to solve. $\boxed{\dfrac{8}{24} = \dfrac{1}{3} = 33\frac{1}{3}\%}$

8 out of 24 teens $\rightarrow \dfrac{8}{24}$

Of the teens surveyed, $33\frac{1}{3}\%$ watch 3 movies a month.

ON YOUR OWN

What percent of the teens surveyed watched 2 or fewer movies each month?

Practice

Building Skills

Use the frequency table to answer questions 1–7.

1. How many teens surveyed do not watch sporting events?

_____

2. How many teens surveyed watch 5 sporting events each week?

_____

3. What is the greatest number of sporting events teens watch in one week?

_____

Sporting Events Teens Watch in One Week

Number of Events	Tally	Frequency
0	II	2
1	IIII	4
2	THL	5
3	THL THL	10
4	THL	5
5	II	2
6	II	2

4. Which number of events has the greatest frequency (appears most often)?

_____

5. How many teens watch 3 events each week?

_____

6. How many teens were surveyed?

_____

7. Five teens watch 4 sporting events each week. What number of sporting events has the same frequency?

_____

Problem Solving

Use the frequency table above to answer questions 8–13.

8. How many teens watch 0–1 sporting events each week?

9. What percent of the teens surveyed watch 0–1 sporting events each week?

10. How many teens watch 2–3 sporting events each week?

11. What percent of the teens surveyed watch 2–3 sporting events each week?

12. What percent of the teens surveyed watch 4 or more sporting events each week?

13. Do you think the results of this survey would be the same in your class? Explain.

Name _____ Date _____

LESSON 41 **Sampling**

Sometimes it is just not possible to gather all the data about a large group, such as all the students in your school or all the fish in the ocean. Instead, you can take a sample of the larger group, or *population*. A **random sample** is a chosen group that closely represents the larger group.

The student council wanted to find out which type of lunch high-school students like the most. Instead of asking all 1,800 students, they asked every fourth person that came into the lunchroom until they had surveyed 200 students. Here are the results of their random sample survey.

Random Sample of 200 High-School Students

Favorite Lunch	Number of Responses
Pizza	75
Tacos	45
Hamburger	55
Spaghetti	25

Example

Using the random sample data, about how many of the 1,800 high-school students would choose pizza?

STEP 1 Write a ratio using the number that represents the item being questioned to the number of people surveyed in the sample.

$$\frac{75}{200}$$

STEP 2 Use ratios to form a proportion between the sample and the entire population.

$$\frac{75}{200} = \frac{n}{1,800}$$

STEP 3 Solve.

If the whole school was surveyed, about 675 students would choose pizza for lunch.

$$\frac{75}{200} = \frac{n}{1,800}$$
$$200n = 135,000$$
$$n = 675$$

ON YOUR OWN

How many of the 1,800 high-school students would choose tacos for lunch?

Practice

Building Skills

Use the random sample survey results to answer questions 1–6.

Random Sample of 200
High-School Students

Favorite Sport	Number of Responses
Soccer	66
Baseball	30
Basketball	60
Hockey	24
Tennis	20

1. How many students were surveyed?

_____

2. How many sport choices could students choose from?

_____

3. What percent of the students chose the least popular sport?

_____

4. What percent of the students surveyed chose baseball?

_____

5. Which sport got twice as many votes as baseball?

_____

6. The high school randomly sampled 200 of the 1,500 students. How many students were *not* surveyed?

_____

Problem Solving

Use the random sample survey results to answer questions 7–12.

7. About how many of the 1,500 students in the school would choose soccer?

8. About how many of the 1,500 students would choose baseball?

9. About how many of the 1,500 students in the high school would choose hockey?

10. About how many of the 1,500 students in the high school would choose tennis?

11. About how many of the 1,500 students in the high school would choose basketball?

12. Would you expect the same results from a random sample using these 5 sports at your school? Explain.

Name _____ Date _____

LESSON 42 Choosing a Graph to Display Data

You have studied different types of graphs and the type of data best suited for each. Look at the multi-bar graph to the right. This graph shows medals awarded to each country at the 2004 Summer Olympics.

A multi-bar graph is one of many ways to display data.

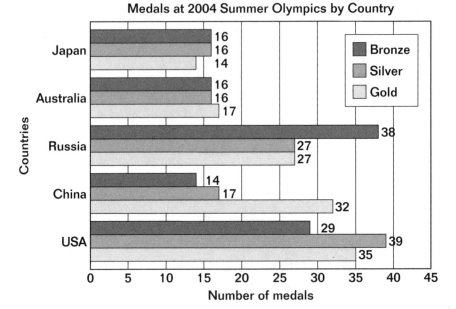

Medals at 2004 Summer Olympics by Country

- The **multi-bar graph** shows three sets of countable data. Notice how the bar graph makes it easy to count and compare the number of medals won by each country.
- A **circle graph** would make it easy to compare the total number of medals awarded to each country.
- A **line graph** is not a good graph to use for this type of data. Line graphs show continuing change in data or how data changes over time.

Example

How many medals did Russia win at the 2004 Olympics?

STEP 1 How does the graph display the data?
The bar graph shows the number of medals of each type won by each country.

STEP 2 Identify the data you need from the graph.
Russia won 27 gold medals, 27 silver medals, and 38 bronze medals.

STEP 3 Use the data to solve the problem.
27 + 27 + 38 = 92

Russia won 92 medals at the 2004 Summer Olympics.

ON YOUR OWN

Which two countries combined won about $\frac{1}{4}$ of the total medals awarded to these 5 countries at the 2004 Summer Olympics?

Number Concepts, Decimals, and Graphs, SV 0435-2

Practice

Building Skills

Use the Olympic multi-bar graph on page 92 to answer questions 1–6.

1. How many gold medals did the United States win?

_____

2. Which country won close to the same number of gold medals as the United States?

_____

3. Which country won about 25% of the medals awarded to these five countries?

_____

4. Which country won more bronze medals than the United States?

_____

5. Which country won close to $\frac{1}{3}$ of the medals awarded to these five countries?

_____

6. Identify those countries that won fewer than 20 bronze medals.

_____

Choose a bar, circle, or line graph for the data. Explain your choice.

7. the number of seats available in each section of the arena where the opening ceremonies take place

_____

8. the temperature readings throughout the opening day of the Olympics

_____

Problem Solving

Use the Olympic multi-bar graph on page 92 to answer questions 9–12.

9. Which two countries won more gold medals than silver or bronze medals?

10. How many more medals did Russia win than Australia?

11. There were 929 medals awarded at the Olympic Games. Estimate the percent of medals awarded to the 5 countries.

12. Did the five countries together win more than 100 bronze medals? Explain.

Name _____   Date _____

LESSON 43 Recognizing Misleading Graphs

Ms. Wilson made these two graphs to show how her classes did on a government test.

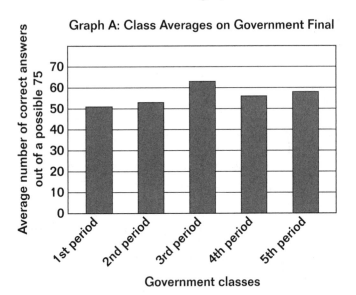

Why do these graphs look so different? Which graph better shows the test results?
- Notice that the **y-axis** goes from **0 to 75** on Graph A, and from **50 to 64** on Graph B.
- Notice that the **y-axis intervals** are spaced by **fives** on Graph A and by **twos** on Graph B.

Graph B makes it look as if there is a big difference between each class's test scores, but this is not true! Graph B is *misleading*!

Example

Graph B says that the 3rd-period class had test scores better than twice the scores for the 4th-period class. Is this true or false? Explain.

STEP 1 **Identify the graph item(s) in the question.**
The 3rd-period score is 63 and the 4th-period score is 56.

STEP 2 **Compare the graph items.**
The scores for these two class periods are different by only seven points. If the 3rd-period class scored more than twice what the 4th-period class scored, then their scores would be higher than 63 points!

STEP 3 **Report your findings.**
The 3rd-period class test scores were not more than twice that of the 4th-period class. If this were true, the 4th-period class would have scored less than 30. The real score of the 4th-period class was 56.

ON YOUR OWN

Graph A shows that the 1st-period class and 2nd-period class did about the same on the test. Is this true or false? Explain.

Practice

Building Skills

Use the Government Class Averages graphs on page 94 to answer questions 1–10.

1. Which graph shows a big difference in how well each class did?

_____

2. Which graph shows a range (from lowest score to highest) of 75 points on the test?

_____

3. Which graph shows intervals of 2 along the *y*-axis?

_____

4. Which graph shows that many of the classes had about the same test results?

_____

5. How many government classes does Ms. Wilson teach?

_____

6. How many class periods have an average score greater than 55 points?

_____

7. Which class period has the lowest average score?

_____

8. What was the average number of questions the 3rd-period class got incorrect?

_____

9. If you made a graph of your test scores, would you start your graph at 0 along the *y*-axis? Explain.

_____

10. If you changed the intervals on Graph A to two instead of five, would the graph look different? Explain.

_____

Problem Solving

Use the Government Class Averages graphs on page 94 to answer questions 11–16.

11. What is the difference between the highest and lowest class average score?

12. What is the ratio of correct answers to total answers for the 1st-period class?

13. Estimate the percent correct for the 1st-period class.

14. If the graphs showed the percent correct instead of the number of correct answers for each class, what value would be at the top of the *y*-axis? Explain.

15. Would Graph A and Graph B look different if percent correct were shown instead of number of correct answers? Explain.

16. Do you think these five classes did well on the test? Explain.

Multiplying Decimals

Multiplying decimals is similar to multiplying whole numbers. However, when multiplying decimals you need to be mindful of the number of decimal places in each factor. The total number of decimal places in the numbers you are multiplying will tell you the number of decimal places in your answer.

EXAMPLE

Multiply. 28.3×6

STEP 1 Multiply.

(Ignore the decimal point for now.)

$$
\begin{array}{r}
\overset{4\ 1}{28.3} \\
\times\ \ 6 \\
\hline
1698
\end{array}
$$

STEP 2 Count the number of decimal places in each number you are multiplying.

STEP 3 Add the number of decimal places and write the number beside the answer (product).

$$
\begin{array}{r}
28.3 \longleftarrow 1 \text{ decimal place} \\
\times\ 6 \longleftarrow 0 \text{ decimal places} \\
\hline
1698 \longleftarrow 1 \text{ decimal place}
\end{array}
$$

STEP 4 Look at the number of decimal places written beside the answer. Starting at the right side of the answer, count that number of decimal places to the left, and put the decimal point there.

$$
\begin{array}{r}
28.3 \longleftarrow 1 \text{ decimal place} \\
\times\ 6 \longleftarrow 0 \text{ decimal places} \\
\hline
169.8 \longleftarrow 1 \text{ decimal place}
\end{array}
$$

The product of 28.3 and 6 is 169.8.

$28.3 \times 6 = 169.8$

Dividing Decimals

Division with decimals is similar to division with whole numbers. However, you must follow some simple guidelines regarding the decimal point when dividing with decimals. If your divisor is not a decimal, but your dividend is, you simply move the decimal point in the dividend up into the quotient. If your divisor is a decimal, then you move the decimal point to the right until your divisor is a whole number. You must also move the decimal point in the dividend the same number of places.

EXAMPLE

Divide. $1.21 \div 2.75$

STEP 1 Set up the problem.

$$2.75\overline{)1.21}$$

STEP 2 Count the number of decimals places in the divisor—the number you are dividing with.

The divisor has two decimal places to the right of the decimal point.

$$2.75\overline{)1.21}$$
2 decimal places ⬩⬩

STEP 3 Move the decimal point in the divisor as many places as there are decimal places in the divisor. Move the decimal point in the dividend (the number being divided) the same number of places.

Move the decimal points two places to the right.

$$2.75\overline{)1.21}$$

STEP 4 Divide. Add zeroes as necessary.

```
        44
275.)121.00
    110 0
     11 00
     11 00
         0
```

STEP 5 Look at the decimal point in the dividend. Place a decimal point directly above it in the quotient. If the decimal point falls to the left of the first digit in the quotient, place a zero to the left of the decimal point.

```
       0.44
275.)121.00
    110 0
     11 00
     11 00
         0
```

$$1.21 \div 2.75 = 0.44$$

Glossary

absolute value (page 34)
the number's distance from zero, which is always positive

addition (page 18)
putting numbers together to find a total

bar graph (page 72)
a graph that uses vertical or horizontal bars to show countable data

base (page 42)
a factor

circle graph (page 76)
a graph that shows how parts of a whole are related to the whole and to each other

comparing numbers (page 12)
determining which whole number is greater than the other or if the numbers are equal

compatible number (page 16)
a number that is close to the an original number, but rounded so as to make it easier to use in problem solving

cube (page 40)
a number with an exponent of 3

decimal (page 46)
number with decimal point; the numbers to the left of the decimal point are whole numbers and the numbers to the right of the decimal point are values less than 1

decimal point (page 46)
separates a whole number from a decimal, a number or part of a number that is less than 1

denominator (page 66)
the bottom number in a fraction

difference (page 20)
the answer to a subtraction problem

digit (page 46)
one of the ten symbols used to write numbers

distributive property (page 24)
property that allows you to split a number or operation being multiplied into two parts, then multiply each part by the second number separately and add the results

dividend (page 26)
the amount being divided

division (page 26)
an operation that separates an amount into parts or finds out how many times a number can fit into another

divisor (page 26)
the number you divide by

double bar graph (page 74)
a graph that uses vertical or horizontal bars to show two sets of countable data

double line graph (page 70)
a graph that shows continuous change of two sets of related data

equivalent (page 66)
the same in value

estimating (page 16)
find an answer by rounding the numbers

estimation (page 16)
to arrive at a reasonably close answer to an exact number

expanded form (page 10)
form of a whole number in which the place value of each digit in a is written separately

exponent (page 36)
a number that tells how many equal factors there are

factors (page 36)
the numbers that are multiplied together to make another number

fraction (page 66)
a whole divided into any number of parts, usually the top number is smaller than the bottom one

frequency table (page 80)
a table that shows the number of times an event occurs

histogram (page 86)
a graph in which bars represent the number of times that data occur within certain intervals or periods

hundredth (page 46)
a decimal with two places to the right of the decimal point

integer (page 28)
positive numbers, negative numbers, and zero

lead digit (page 16)
the first digit on the left in a number with two or more digits; in the number 1,276, the 1 is the lead digit

line graph (page 68)
a graph that shows continuous changes in data

line plot (page 80)
a graph that organizes data on a number line; it is good for showing the range of data

multi-bar graph (page 92)
a bar graph with three or more sets of bars of countable data

multiplication (page 22)
combining equal numbers two or more times to get a total

negative number (page 28)
a number less than zero

negative relationship (page 82)
when one set of values in a data set increases while the other set tends to decrease

number line (page 28)
a line with equally spaced points that are labeled with numbers

numerator (page 66)
the top number in a fraction

order of operations (page 44)
the correct order in which operations must be done to solve problems

ordering numbers (page 12)
arranging the whole numbers from least to greatest or greatest to least

place value (page 10)
the value of an individual digit depending upon its location within a greater number

place-value chart (page 10)
shows the value of each digit in a whole or decimal number by displaying each digit's location (tenths, hundredths, etc.)

positive number (page 28)
a number greater than zero

positive relationship (page 82)
when one set of values in a data set increases while the other set also tends to increase

power (page 42)
an exponent

product (page 22)
the answer to a multiplication problem

quotient (page 26)
the answer to a division problem

random sample (page 90)
a chosen group that closely represents a larger group

rounding decimals (page 50)
approximating the value of a decimal number or numbers to make it or them easier to work with

scatter plot (page 82)
a graph of ordered pairs of numbers that show events

square (page 36)
a number with an exponent of 2

square number (page 36)
the product of two identical numbers

square root (page 38)
the number that is multiplied by itself to get the given number

standard form (page 10)
a whole number written with digits; each digit's position in the number identifies its place value

stem-and-leaf plot (page 84)
a way to organize data that shows how that data are spread and where they cluster; the stem identifies the leading digit or digits and the leaf identifies the digit in the ones place

subtraction (page 20)
taking away a certain amount from another amount to find a difference

sum (page 18)
the answer to an addition problem

survey (page 88)
an informal poll

tenth (page 46)
a decimal that sits one place to the right of the decimal point

thousandth (page 46)
decimal that sits three places to the right of the decimal point

Venn diagram (page 78)
a drawing of overlapping circles that shows how different sets of data are related to each other

word form (page 10)
a number written with words

x-axis (page 83)
horizontal number line on coordinate plane

y-axis (page 83)
vertical number line on coordinate plane

Answer Key

ASSESSMENT

PAGES 4–8

1. one hundred eighty-five thousand, four hundred five

2. ten thousand

3. The first two digits are the same in both numbers. For the third digits, $6 > 5$, so $40,654 > 40,574$.

4. Use a number line to show that $-2 > -3$.

5. Use a number line to show that $-6 < -4 < 0$.

6. The number following the underlined digit is 5, so the 7 is rounded up to 8. All following digits are replaced by zeros. The number is 148,000.

7. The problem asks for a total, so the numbers are added. $950 + 260 = 1,210$

8. The problem asks for a difference, so the numbers are subtracted. $860 \text{ cans} - 725 \text{ cans} = 135 \text{ cans}$

9. $4,309 + 705 = 5,014$

10. $1,308 - 129 = 1,179$

11. Use a number line to solve. $-14 + 6 = -(14 - 6) = -8$

12. Use a number line to solve. $-14 - 6 = -(14 + 6) = -20$

13. The problem asks for a difference, so the numbers are subtracted. $6 - 8 = -2$

14. $6 \times (30 + 4) = 6 \times 30 + 6 \times 4 = 180 + 24 = 204$

15. $32 \times 219 = 7,008$

16. $1,458 \div 27 = 54$

17. The signs are different, so the quotient is negative. $45 \div (-5) = -9$

18. The signs are the same, so the product will be positive. $-6 \times (-8) = 48$

19. $10 \text{ days} \times -2°F/\text{day} = -20°F$

20. $945 \text{ miles} \div 50 \text{ miles/hour} = 18.9 \text{ hours}$

21. $|-22| = 22$

22. $|9| = 9$

23. $8^2 = 8 \times 8 = 64$

24. $7 \times 7 = 49$, so $\sqrt{49} = 7$

25. $4^3 = 4 \times 4 \times 4 = 64$

26. $6^5 \times 6^9 = 6^{5+9} = 6^{14}$

27. 45.46

28. 3.071

29. 16.019

30. 0.605

31. 1 hundredth

32. 3 tenths

33. 1 hundredth

34. 0.5

35. 17.5

36. 1.0

37. $0.378 < 0.4$

38. $7.379 > 7.37$

39. $0.72 < 1.7$

40. $0.109, 0.19, 0.91, 1.9$

41. $47.05, 47.205, 47.500, 47.52$

42. $6.465 + 143.78 = 150.245$

43. $9.003 + 18.34 = 27.343$

44. $7.45 - 3.76 = 3.69$

45. $32.9 - 6.37 = 26.53$

46. $30.6 \times 3 = 91.8$

47. $320 \div 0.4 = 800$

48. $0.62 \times 42 = 26.04$

49. $3,864 \div 9.2 = 420$

50. $0.75 = \frac{75}{100} = \frac{3}{4}$

51. $\frac{7}{10} = 0.7$

52. $0.9 = \frac{9}{10}$

53. $\frac{3}{100} = 0.03$

54. $8.4 \times 5 = 42.0$ minutes

55. $609.88 - 145.90 = 463.98$; $463.98

56. spring; point on line for boys above point on line for girls

57. spring; lines are closest in spring

58. November; 400 vs. 200

59. December; 375 dimes

60. gold; gold is about half the circle

61. bronze; bronze sector of graph is less than $\frac{1}{4}$ of the circle

62. about $25 to $40

63. from $40 to $60

64. True; it appears that there is a positive correlation between earnings and savings.

LESSON 1

PAGE 10

ON YOUR OWN: 90 thousand or 9 ten thousands

PAGE 11

1. twenty-eight thousand, one hundred seventy-five

2. two hundred fifteen thousand, one hundred twenty-five

3. 54,160

4. 405,627

5. 175,946

6. Use a place value chart to determine that the value of the digit is 20 thousand.

7. Use a place-value chart to determine that the value of the digit is 8 hundred thousand.

8. Use a place-value chart to determine that the value of the digit is 5 thousand.

9. Use a place-value chart to determine that the value of the digit is zero hundreds.

10. one hundred twenty-five thousand, three hundred forty-five

11. eight million, five hundred forty-two thousand, three hundred forty-nine

12. $9,763,000 = 9,000,000 + 700,000 + 60,000 + 3,000$

13. $1,030,402 = 1,000,000 + 30,000 + 400 + 2$

14. Use a place-value chart to determine that the value of the digit is 90 thousand.

15. Use a place-value chart to determine that the value of the digit is 2 hundred thousand.

LESSON 2

PAGE 12

ON YOUR OWN: 402,682 > 402,197

PAGE 13

1. The first digit is different.
   6 > 5, so 647 > 592

2. The first digit is the same.
   3 < 6, so 536 < 563

3. The first digit is the same.
   7 > 2, so 872 > 827

4. The first two digits are the same.
   5 < 6, so 2,759 < 2,765

5. The first digit is the same.
   1 > 0, so 3,152 > 3,025

6. The first digit is the same.
   0 < 1, so 1,024 < 1,127

7. The first digit is the same.
   1 > 0, so 6,139 > 6,029

8. The first digit is the same.
   5 < 6, so 25,094 < 26,303

9. The first three digits are the same.
   0 < 7, so 512,057 < 512,750

10. The first digit is the same.
    2 > 1, so 1,251 > 1,137
    The distance from Kansas City to Boston is greater.

11. The first digit is the same.
    9 > 3, so 298 > 232

12. The first digit is the same.
    9 > 8, so 29,619 > 28,210
    Attendance was lower in 2003.

13. The first two digits are the same.
    3 > 0, so 1,730 > 1,703
    The Duvals drove farther.

14. The first three digits are the same.
    7 > 6, so 54,076 > 54,067
    Yuri scored more points.

15. The first digit is the same.
    4 > 3, so 543 > 534
    Meg collected more.

LESSON 3

PAGE 14

ON YOUR OWN: 47,600

PAGE 15

1. The underlined digit is in the tens place. The following digit is 2, so the underlined digit is unchanged. The rounded number is 340.

2. The underlined digit is in the hundreds place. The following digit is 5, so the underlined digit will be rounded up. The rounded number is 1,400.

3. The underlined digit is in the hundreds place. The following digit, 1, is less than 5, so the underlined digit is unchanged. The rounded number is 500.

4. The underlined digit is in the tens place. The following digit is 5, so the underlined digit will be rounded up. The rounded number is 740.

5. The underlined digit is in the thousands place. The following digit, 3, is less than 5, so the underlined digit is unchanged. The rounded number is 4,000.

6. The underlined digit is in the hundreds place. The following digit is greater than 5, so the underlined digit will be rounded up. The rounded number is 400.

7. The underlined digit is in the tens place. The following digit, 4, is less than 5, so the underlined digit is unchanged. The rounded number is 850.

8. The underlined digit is in the tens place. The following digit, 8, is greater than 5, so the underlined digit will be rounded up. The rounded number is 12,140.

9. The underlined digit is in the hundreds place. The following digit, 0, is less than 5, so the underlined digit is unchanged. The rounded number is 6,300.

10. The underlined digit is in the ten thousands place. The following digit, 2, is less than 5, so the underlined digit is unchanged. The rounded number is 40,000.

11. The underlined digit is in the tens place. The following digit is 9, so the underlined digit will be rounded up. The rounded number is 1,640.

12. The underlined digit is in the thousands place. The following digit is 1, so the underlined digit is unchanged. The rounded number is 57,000.

13. The digit 8 is in the thousands place. The following digit, 9, is greater than 5, so the 8 will be rounded up. The rounded number is 9,000.

14. The digit 3 is in the hundreds place. The following digit, 4, is less than 5, so 3 is unchanged. The rounded number is 19,300.

15. The digit 0 is in the tens place. The following digit is 5, so the 0 will be rounded up. The rounded number is 310.

16. The digit 1 is in the hundreds place. The following digit, 6, is greater than 5, so the 1 will be rounded up. The rounded number is 4,200.

17. The digit 7 is in the tens place. The following digit, 9, is greater than 5, so the 7 will be rounded up. The rounded number is 2,580.

18. The digit 1 is in the hundreds place. The following digit, 3, is less than 5, so the 1 is unchanged. The rounded number is 1,100.

LESSON 4

PAGE 16
ON YOUR OWN: about 2,000
PAGE 17

1. $4,000 + 100 = 4,100$
2. $800 - 300 = 500$
3. $300 + 700 = 1,000$
4. $600 - 200 = 400$
5. $2,000 + 1,000 = 3,000$
6. $4,000 - 1,000 = 3,000$
7. $20 + 20 = 40$
8. $90 + 10 = 100$
9. $200 + 100 = 300$ or $170 + 130 = 300$
10. $300 + 600 = 900$
11. The problem asks for a difference, so the numbers are subtracted.
    100 stories $-$ 80 stories $= 20$ stories
12. The problem asks for a total, so the numbers are added.
    500 votes $+$ 300 votes $= 800$ votes
13. The problem asks for a difference, so the numbers are subtracted.
    $55,000 - 52,000 = 3,000$
14. The problem asks for a total, so the numbers are added.
    5 hours $+$ 4 hours $= 9$ hours
15. The problem asks for a difference, so the numbers are subtracted.
    12,000 pounds $-$ 2,000 pounds $= 10,000$ pounds
    (also acceptable: 12,000 pounds $-$ 1,600 pounds $= 10,400$ pounds)
16. The problem asks for a total, so the numbers are added.
    600 people $+$ 600 people $= 1,200$ people
    (also acceptable: 630 people $+$ 570 people $= 1,200$ people)

LESSON 5

PAGE 18
ON YOUR OWN: $748 + 215 = 963$
PAGE 19

1. $532 + 159 = 691$
2. $2,403 + 829 = 3,232$
3. $812 + 249 = 1,061$
4. $2,147 + 315 = 2,462$
5. $214 + 639 = 853$
6. $315 + 179 = 494$
7. $786 + 457 = 1,243$
8. $3,075 + 542 = 3,617$
9. $1,892 + 248 = 2,140$
10. 1,835 pounds $+$ 891 pounds $= 2,726$ pounds
11. 1,235 points $+$ 784 points $= 2,019$ points
12. 234 minutes $+$ 268 minutes $= 502$ minutes
13. 137 CDs $+$ 53 CDs $= 190$ CDs
14. 1,464 flowers $+$ 1,374 flowers $= 2,838$ flowers
15. 873 people $+$ 1,273 people $= 2,146$ people

LESSON 6

PAGE 20
ON YOUR OWN: $225 - 78 = 147$
PAGE 21

1. $872 - 128 = 744$
2. $1,629 - 348 = 1,281$
3. $706 - 129 = 577$
4. $513 - 89 = 424$
5. $538 - 175 = 363$
6. $435 - 239 = 196$
7. $731 - 175 = 556$
8. $1,247 - 309 = 938$
9. $3,428 - 759 = 2,669$
10. 692 tickets $-$ 64 tickets $= 628$ tickets
11. 345 houses $-$ 63 houses $= 282$ houses
12. 248 miles $-$ 179 miles $= 69$ miles
13. 450 stamps $-$ 219 stamps $= 231$ stamps
14. 1,050 minutes $-$ 628 minutes $= 422$ minutes
15. 800 T-shirts $-$ 189 T-shirts $= 611$ T-shirts

LESSON 7

PAGE 22
ON YOUR OWN: $78 \times 25 = 1,950$
PAGE 23

1. $52 \times 36 = 1,872$
2. $24 \times 16 = 384$
3. $91 \times 43 = 3,913$
4. $34 \times 28 = 952$
5. $326 \times 12 = 3,912$
6. $140 \times 74 = 10,360$
7. $308 \times 26 = 8,008$
8. $352 \times 24 = 8,448$
9. $106 \times 39 = 4,134$
10. 36 boxes $\times$ 16 hats/box $= 576$ hats
11. 38 messages/day $\times$ 17 days $= 646$ messages
12. 15 stories $\times$ 18 offices/story $= 270$ offices $= 270$ connections
13. 431 pieces/model $\times$ 65 models $= 28,015$ pieces

LESSON 8

PAGE 24
ON YOUR OWN: $4 \times (5 + 20) = (4 \times 5) + (4 \times 20) = 20 + 80 = 100$
PAGE 25

1. $9 \times (20 + 4) = (9 \times 20) + (9 \times 4) = 180 + 36 = 216$
2. $7 \times (10 + 5) = (7 \times 10) + (7 \times 5) = 70 + 35 = 105$
3. $6 \times (30 + 3) = (30 \times 6) + (3 \times 6) = 180 + 18 = 198$
4. $3 \times (5 + 20) = (3 \times 5) + (3 \times 20) = 15 + 60 = 75$
5. $9 \times (10 + 6) = (9 \times 10) + (9 \times 6) = 90 + 54 = 144$
6. $8 \times (10 + 4) = (10 \times 8) + (4 \times 8) = 80 + 32 = 112$

7. $5 \times (20 + 7) = (20 \times 5) + (7 \times 5) = 100 + 35 = 135$

8. $4 \times (30 + 6) = (4 \times 30) + (4 \times 6) = 120 + 24 = 144$

9. $8 \times (20 + 6) = (8 \times 20) + (8 \times 6) = 160 + 48 = 208$

10. $9 \times (20 + 3) = (20 \times 9) + (3 \times 9) = 180 + 27 = 207$

11. $18 \times 3 = 3 \times (10 + 8) = (10 \times 3) + (8 \times 3) = 30 + 24$
$= 54$ miles

12. $4 \times 28 = 4 \times (20 + 8) = (4 \times 20) + (4 \times 8) = 80 + 32$
$= 112$ CDs

13. $43 \times 2 = 2 \times (40 + 3) = (40 \times 2) + (3 \times 2) = 80 + 6$
$= 86$ cups

14. $8 \times 17 = 8 \times (10 + 7) = (8 \times 10) + (8 \times 7) = 80 + 56$
$= 136$ points

15. $42 \times 9 = 9 \times (40 + 2) = (40 \times 9) + (2 \times 9) = 360 + 18$
$= 378$ pints

16. $3 \times 24 = 3 \times (20 + 4) = (3 \times 20) + (3 \times 4) = 60 + 12$
$= 72$ problems

LESSON 9

PAGE 26

ON YOUR OWN: $1{,}235 \div 65 = 19$

PAGE 27

1. $53\overline{)2385}$ quotient 45

2. $21\overline{)504}$ quotient 24

3. $25\overline{)3{,}225}$ quotient 129

4. $38\overline{)836}$ quotient 22

5. $81\overline{)729}$ quotient 9

6. $23\overline{)3{,}956}$ quotient 172

7. $63\overline{)1{,}827}$ quotient 29

8. $34\overline{)3{,}876}$ quotient 114

9. $41\overline{)8{,}118}$ quotient 198

10. $15\overline{)645}$ boxes quotient 43

11. $22\overline{)3{,}850}$ tickets quotient 175

12. $18\overline{)198}$ days quotient 11

13. $12\overline{)3{,}960}$ tickets quotient 330

LESSON 10

PAGE 28

ON YOUR OWN: Fairbanks, Alaska

PAGE 29

1. $-12 > -23$

2. $0 > -8$

3. $5 < 15$

4. $-5 < -4$

5. $-25 < 25$

6. $3 > -1$

7. $9 > 7 > -6$

8. $-12 < -8 < -5$

9. $0 > -5 > -14$

10. $25 > 0 > -4$

11. $16 > 8$; colder

12. $75 > -250$; Tanya

13. $4 > 3$; Matt

14. $2 > 1$; the second test

15. $-7 > -39$; the second half

16. $1{,}450 > 1{,}381 > 1{,}250$; the Sears Tower

LESSON 11

PAGE 30

ON YOUR OWN: $-7 - (-3) = -7 + 3 = -4$

PAGE 31

1. $-3 - (-6) = 3$

2. $7 + (-2) = 5$

3. $-6 + (-4) = -10$

4. $6 + (-4) = 2$

5. $7 - (-5) = 12$

6. $-7 - (-5) = -2$

7. $-7 + 5 = -2$

8. $6 + (-8) = -2$

9. $-6 + (-8) = -14$

10. $-6 - (-8) = 2$

11. $-5 + (-6) = -11$; 11 feet below the surface

12. $-3 + 2 = -1$; 1 stroke under par

13. $5 - (-2) = 7$; increased by $7°F$

14. $-60 - (-45) = -15$; Monday

15. $-156 - (-12) = -144$; 144 meters

16. $(60 - 3) - 4 = 53$ minutes

LESSON 12

PAGE 32

ON YOUR OWN: $-5 \times 12 = -60$ feet

PAGE 33

1. The signs are the same, so the product is positive.
$-12 \times (-3) = 36$.

2. The signs are different, so the product is negative.
$12 \times (-3) = -36$

3. The signs are different, so the product is negative.
$-3 \times (20) = -60$

4. The signs are the same, so the product is positive.
$-3 \times (-20) = 60$

5. The signs are different, so the quotient is negative.
$-15 \div 5 = -3$

6. The signs are the same, so the quotient is positive.
$-15 \div (-5) = 3$

7. The signs are different, so the quotient is negative.
$15 \div (-5) = -3$

8. The signs are different, so the quotient is negative.
$24 \div (-6) = -4$

9. The signs are the same, so the product is positive.
$-6 \times (-4) = 24$

10. The signs are the same, so the quotient is positive.
$-24 \div (-6) = 4$

11. The signs are different, so the product is negative.
$5 \times (-12) = -60$; -60 feet

12. The signs are different, so the product is negative.
$10 \times (-20) = -200$; -200 gallons

13. The signs are the same, so the product is positive.
$25 \times (8) = 200$; 200 gallons

14. The signs are the same, so the product will be positive.
$6 \times (15) = 90$; 90 new CDs

15. The signs are different, so the product is negative.
$8 \times (-3) = -24$; drops 24°

16. The signs are different, so the product is negative.
$3 \times (-2) = -6$; 6 strokes under par

LESSON 13

PAGE 34

ON YOUR OWN: $|-6| > |-4|$

PAGE 35

1. $|-17| = 17$ **2.** $|5| = 5$ **3.** $|-25| = 25$

4. $|-12| = 12$ **5.** $|-37| = 37$ **6.** $|-10| = 10$

7. $|15| < |-16|$ because $15 < 16$.

8. $|8| = |-8|$ because $8 = 8$.

9. $-|4| < |24|$ because $4 < 24$.

10. $|-9| > |2|$ because $9 > 2$.

11. $-|-4| < |9|$ because $-4 < 9$.

12. $|12| > |-1|$ because $12 > 1$.

13. $|-15| = 15$ feet dropped

14. $|-3| = 3$ lost points

15. $|-30| = 30$ minutes lost

16. $|-15| = 15°F$ dropped

17. $|3| = 3$ sweaters added

18. $|-75| = 75$ students dropped

19. $|-7| = 7$ yards lost

20. $|12| = 12$ minutes gained

LESSON 14

PAGE 36

ON YOUR OWN: $3^2 = 9$

PAGE 37

1. $5^2 = 5 \times 5 = 25$ **2.** $7^2 = 7 \times 7 = 49$

3. $10^2 = 10 \times 10 = 100$ **4.** $12^2 = 12 \times 12 = 144$

5. $(-5)^2 = (-5) \times (-5) = 25$

6. $(-7)^2 = (-7) \times (-7) = 49$

7. $(-8)^2 = (-8) \times (-8) = 64$

8. $(-9)^2 = (-9) \times (-9) = 81$

9. $(-10)^2 = (-10) \times (-10) = 100$

10. $(-12)^2 = (-12) \times (-12) = 144$

11. $10^2 = 10 \times 10 = 100$ squares

12. $12^2 = 12 \times 12 = 144$ square feet

13. $9^2 = 9 \times 9 = 81$ holes **14.** $4^2 = 4 \times 4 = 16$ pizzas

15. $8^2 = 8 \times 8 = 64$ hours **16.** $6^2 = 6 \times 6 = 36$ ounces

LESSON 15

PAGE 38

ON YOUR OWN: $\sqrt{81} = 9$

PAGE 39

1. $7^2 = 49$, so $\sqrt{49} = 7$ **2.** $8^2 = 64$, so $\sqrt{64} = 8$

3. $5^2 = 25$, so $\sqrt{25} = 5$ **4.** $6^2 = 36$, so $\sqrt{36} = 6$

5. $2^2 = 4$, so $\sqrt{4} = 2$ **6.** $3^2 = 9$, so $\sqrt{9} = 3$

7. $11^2 = 121$, so $\sqrt{121} = 11$ **8.** $10^2 = 100$, so $\sqrt{100} = 10$

9. $12^2 = 144$, so $\sqrt{144} = 12$ **10.** $\sqrt{16} = 4$ feet

11. $\sqrt{36} = 6$ sandwiches **12.** $\sqrt{25} = 5$ letters

13. $\sqrt{49} = 7$ band members **14.** $\sqrt{100} = 10$ feet

15. $\sqrt{144} = 12$ inches

LESSON 16

PAGE 40

ON YOUR OWN: $3^3 = 27 \text{ ft}^3$

PAGE 41

1. $5^3 = (5 \times 5) \times 5 = 25 \times 5 = 125$

2. $10^3 = (10 \times 10) \times 10 = 100 \times 10 = 1,000$

3. $6^3 = (6 \times 6) \times 6 = 36 \times 6 = 216$

4. $9^3 = (9 \times 9) \times 9 = 81 \times 9 = 729$

5. $8^3 = (8 \times 8) \times 8 = 64 \times 8 = 512$

6. $7^3 = (7 \times 7) \times 7 = 49 \times 7 = 343$

7. $1^3 = (1 \times 1) \times 1 = 1 \times 1 = 1$

8. $11^3 = (11 \times 11) \times 11 = 121 \times 11 = 1,331$

9. $15^3 = (15 \times 15) \times 15 = 225 \times 15 = 3,375$

10. $10^3 = (10 \times 10) \times 10 = 100 \times 10 = 1,000$ cubic inches

11. $5^3 = (5 \times 5) \times 5 = 25 \times 5 = 125$ oranges

12. $6^3 = (6 \times 6) \times 6 = 36 \times 6 = 216$ golf balls

13. $15^3 = (15 \times 15) \times 15 = 225 \times 15 = 3,375$ cubic inches

14. $3^3 = (3 \times 3) \times 3 = 9 \times 3 = 27$ cubes

15. $12^3 = (12 \times 12) \times 12 = 144 \times 12 = 1,728$ cubic feet

LESSON 17

PAGE 42

ON YOUR OWN: $5^2 \times 5^4 = 5^6 = 15,625$

PAGE 43

1. $5^4 = 5 \times 5 \times 5 \times 5 = 625$
2. $10^2 \times 10^2 = 10^{2+2} = 10^4 = 10 \times 10 \times 10 \times 10 = 10,000$
3. $8^2 \times 8^1 = 8^{2+1} = 8^3 = 8 \times 8 \times 8 = 512$
4. $12^3 \times 12^3 = 12^6 = 12 \times 12 \times 12 \times 12 \times 12 \times 12 = 2,985,984$
5. $7^3 \times 7^2 = 7^{3+2} = 7^5 = 7 \times 7 \times 7 \times 7 \times 7 = 16,807$
6. $2^2 \times 2^5 = 2^{2+5} = 2^7 = 2 \times 2 \times 2 \times 2 \times 2 \times 2 \times 2 = 128$
7. $1^2 \times 1^3 = 1^{3+2} = 1^5 = 1 \times 1 \times 1 \times 1 \times 1 = 1$
8. $9^4 \times 9^3 = 9^7 = 9 \times 9 \times 9 \times 9 \times 9 \times 9 \times 9 = 4,782,969$
9. $4^2 \times 4^2 = 4^{2+2} = 4^4 = 4 \times 4 \times 4 \times 4 = 256$
10. $3^5 \times 3^2 = 3^7 = 3 \times 3 \times 3 \times 3 \times 3 \times 3 \times 3 = 2,187$
11. $3^3 \times 3^1 = 3^{3+1} = 3^4 = 3 \times 3 \times 3 \times 3 = 81$
12. $2^2 \times 2^3 = 2^{2+3} = 2^5 = 2 \times 2 \times 2 \times 2 \times 2 = 32$
13. $4^3 \times 4^6 \times 4^2 = 4^{3+6+2} = 4^{11} = 4,194,304$
14. $6^2 \times 6^3 = 6^5 = 6 \times 6 \times 6 \times 6 \times 6 = 7,776$
15. $2^8 \times 2^4 = 2^{12} = 2 \times 2 \times 2 \times 2 \times 2 \times 2 \times 2 \times 2 \times 2 \times 2 \times 2 \times 2 = 4,096$
16. $5^5 \times 5^{-3} = 5^{5-3} = 5^2 = 5 \times 5 = 25$

LESSON 18

PAGE 44

ON YOUR OWN: $(6 + 3) \times 2^3 - 3 \times 2 = 66$

PAGE 45

1. $28 - 5 + 3^2 \times 5 = 28 - 5 + 9 \times 5 = 28 - 5 + 45$
   $= 23 + 45 = 68$
2. $2^2 + (5 - 3) \times 3 = 2^2 + 2 \times 3 = 4 + 2 \times 3 = 4 + 6 = 10$
3. $2^2 + 5 - 3 \times 3 = 4 + 5 - 3 \times 3 = 4 + 5 - 9 = 9 - 9 = 0$
4. $(5 + 9) \times 4 - 8 = 14 \times 4 - 8 = 56 - 8 = 48$
5. $5 + 9 \times 4 - 8 = 5 + 36 - 8 = 41 - 8 = 33$
6. $12 - 5 \times 2^3 - 3 = 12 - 5 \times 8 - 3 = 12 - 40 - 3$
   $= -28 - 3 = -31$
7. $(12 - 5) \times (2^3 - 3) = 7 \times (8 - 3) = 7 \times 5 = 35$
8. $36 - 4 - 4^2 + 5 = 36 - 4 - 16 + 5 = 32 - 16 + 5$
   $= 16 + 5 = 21$
9. $(36 - 4) - (4^2 + 5) = 32 - (16 + 5) = 32 - 21 = 11$
10. $(3 \times \$15) + (2 \times \$12) + \$4 = \$45 + \$24 + \$4$
    $= \$69 + \$4 = \$73$
11. $(4 \times 80) + (3 \times 50) = 320 + 150 = 470 \text{ seats}$
12. $(\$5 \times 30) + (\$1 \times 25) + (\$2 \times 11) = \$150 + \$25 + \$22$
    $= \$175 + \$22 = \$197$

13. $(\$5 \times 120) + (\$3 \times 70) + (\$1 \times 20) = \$600 + \$210 + \$20$
    $= \$810 + \$20 = \$830$
14. $(3 \times 4 \times 6) + (5 \times 4 \times 4) = (12 \times 6) + (20 \times 4)$
    $= 72 + 80 = 152 \text{ bottles}$
15. $\$20 - (\$3 \times 3 + \$2 \times 2) = \$20 - (\$9 + \$4)$
    $= \$20 - \$13 = \$7$

LESSON 19

PAGE 46

ON YOUR OWN: 1 tenth

PAGE 47

1. 7 hundredths
2. 4 thousandths
3. 3 tenths
4. 6 hundredths
5. 7 hundredths
6. 5 hundredths
7. 3 thousandths
8. 9 hundredths
9. 3 hundredths
10. 7 tenths
11. The tenths place is directly to the right of the decimal point. A decimal is a number that contains a decimal point; so all digits in the number are part of the decimal. Of the choices, 6.87 is the only three-digit decimal with 8 in the tenths place.
12. All choices are five-digit decimals, but only 15.009 has the digit 9 in the thousandths place.
13. 10.62 has 6 in the tenths place. If second place is 2 tenths greater, then the tenths place in this decimal is $6 + 2 = 8$. Tenths place is the only place that changes, so the second place time is 10.82 seconds.
14. All choices have six digits except 23.783; 234.736 and 321.742 have a 7 in tenths place and an even digit in thousandths place. In 321.742, the 4 in the hundredths place is twice the 2 in thousandths place. The mystery number is 321.742.
15. Order all the choices from greatest to least: 0.217, 0.213, 0.207, 0.035, 0.025. Place Adrian's average between 0.217 and 0.213. The only average greater than Adrian's is 0.217.

LESSON 20

PAGE 48

ON YOUR OWN: 12.85

PAGE 49

1. 1.465
2. 12.079
3. 0.48
4. 2.7
5. 9.02
6. 8.014
7. 34.008
8. 698.03
9. 3.5
10. 325.26
11. 5.02 pounds
12. 2.4 blocks
13. 0.406
14. 26.3 miles
15. 0.21 second
16. 3.26 inches
17. 2.6 ounces
18. 31.3 inches

LESSON 21

ON YOUR OWN: 4.76

1. The digit 6 is in tenths place. The following digit, 7, is greater than 5, so the 6 is rounded up. To the nearest tenth, the decimal is 34.7.

2. The digit 3 is in tenths place. The following digit, 6, is greater than 5, so the 3 is rounded up. To the nearest tenth, the decimal is 8.4.

3. The digit 6 is in tenths place. The following digit is less than 5, so the 6 remains the same. To the nearest tenth, the decimal is 143.6.

4. The digit 5 is in hundredths place. The following digit, 6, is greater than 5, so the 5 is rounded up. To the nearest hundredth, the decimal is 9.26.

5. The digit 7 is in hundredths place. The following digit is less than 5, so the 7 remains the same. To the nearest hundredth, the decimal is 6.87.

6. The digit 2 is in hundredths place. The following digit, 3, is less than 5, so the 2 remains the same. To the nearest hundredth, the decimal is 0.72.

7. The digit 2 is in thousandths place. The following digit, 1, is less than 5, so the 2 remains the same. To the nearest thousandth, the decimal is 132.452.

8. The digit 0 is in thousandths place. The following digit, 1, is less than 5, so the 0 remains the same. To the nearest thousandth, the decimal is 79.990.

9. The digit 9 is in tenths place in the answer. If this was rounded up, the initial digit in tenths place was 8, and the digit following it must be 5 or greater. The only choice possible is 34.87.

10. The digit 2 is in ones place. The original number had either 1 in ones place with a digit in tenths place that was 5 or greater, or 2 in ones place with a digit in tenths place that was less than 5. Only choice is 11.47.

11. The digit 6 is in tenths place. The following digit is 5, so the 6 is rounded up to 7. The tadpole is 3.7 inches long.

12. The digit 8 is in ones place. The following digit is 5, so the 8 is rounded up to 9. She pays $9 for lunch.

LESSON 22

ON YOUR OWN: 6.45

1. $0.50 = 0.50$ 2. $1.40 < 1.45$ 3. $0.64 < 0.69$
4. $7.05 < 7.50$ 5. $0.400 = 0.400$ 6. $0.394 = 0.394$

7. Write the decimals with the same number of places: 0.70, 0.07, 0.17, 1.70. Compare and order the numbers: $0.07 < 0.17 < 0.70 < 1.70$. The order from least to greatest is 0.07, 0.17, 0.7, 1.7.

8. Write the decimals with the same number of places: 0.456, 0.450, 0.500, 0.405. Compare and order the numbers: $0.405 < 0.450 < 0.456 < 0.500$. The order from least to greatest is 0.405, 0.45, 0.456, 0.5.

9. Write the decimals with the same number of places: 11.27, 01.27, 11.20, 12.27. Compare and order the numbers: $12.27 > 11.27 > 11.20 > 01.27$. The order from greatest to least is 12.27, 11.27, 11.2, 1.27.

10. Write the decimals with the same number of places: 0.380, 0.387, 0.370, 0.400. Compare and order the numbers: $0.400 > 0.387 > 0.380 > 0.370$. The order from greatest to least is 0.4, 0.387, 0.380, 0.37.

11. Write the decimals with the same number of places: 1.56, 1.50. Compare and order the numbers: $1.56 > 1.50$. The pitcher that holds 1.56 quarts holds more.

12. Write the decimals with the same number of places: 4.35, 4.70. Compare and order the numbers: $4.70 > 4.35$. More visitors attended in 2003.

13. All decimals are written with the same number of places. Compare and order the numbers: $\$14.65 > \$14.53 > \$13.47$. The refrigerator costs the most to use.

14. All decimals are written with the same number of places. Compare and order the numbers: $1.14 > 0.20 > 0.07$. Anchorage had the most rain in June.

LESSON 23

ON YOUR OWN: $2.5 + 3.56 = 6.06$ ft

1. $25.43 + 32.7 = 58.13$ 2. $1.598 + 12.400 = 13.998$
3. $7.00 + 6.89 = 13.89$ 4. $3.015 + 7.960 = 10.975$
5. $0.476 + 3.790 = 4.266$ 6. $4.109 + 0.470 = 4.579$
7. $8.540 + 2.226 = 10.766$ 8. $3.170 + 8.036 = 11.206$
9. $0.211 + 13.500 = 13.711$ 10. $56.7 + 12.25 = 68.95$
11. 2.70 quarts + 4.09 quarts = 6.79 quarts
12. 4.50 million + 5.95 million = 10.45 million
13. 13.40 yards + 6.98 yards = 20.38 yards
14. 15.57 gallons + 8.00 gallons = 23.57 gallons

LESSON 24

ON YOUR OWN: $29.5 - 18.75 = 10.75$ quarts

PAGE 57

1. $14.93 - 2.74 = 12.19$
2. $1.874 - 0.910 = 0.964$
3. $7.510 - 6.215 = 1.295$
4. $43.706 - 16.910 = 26.796$
5. $0.879 - 0.680 = 0.199$
6. $4.647 - 2.984 = 1.663$
7. $6.230 - 3.985 = 2.245$
8. $4.42 - 1.28 = 3.14$
9. $0.806 - 0.540 = 0.266$
10. $14.714 - 0.029 = 14.685$
11. 5.5 gallons $- 2.6$ gallons $= 2.9$ gallons; 2.9 gallons > 2.5 gallons, so they will have enough paint.
12. 20.75 pints $- 14.60$ pints $= 6.15$ pints
13. 28.34 seconds $- 25.22$ seconds $= 3.12$ seconds
14. $10,179.16$ points $- 10,120.24$ points $= 58.92$ points

LESSON 25

PAGE 58

ON YOUR OWN: $7 \times 1.4 = 9.8$ yards

PAGE 59

1. $9.9 \times 2 = 19.8$
2. $7.2 \times 5 = 36.0$
3. $4.13 \times 9 = 37.17$
4. $61.7 \times 8 = 493.6$
5. $0.45 \times 7 = 3.15$
6. $27.4 \times 13 = 356.2$
7. $1.32 \times 21 = 27.72$
8. $12.5 \times 12 = 150.0$
9. $60.1 \times 32 = 1,923.2$
10. 3.5 yards/doll $\times 9$ dolls $= 31.5$ yards
11. 34.5 miles/gallon $\times 14$ gallons $= 483.0$ miles
12. 8.5 hours/person $\times 3$ persons $= 25.5$ hours
13. 4.5 gallons/container $\times 12$ containers $= 54.0$ gallons

LESSON 26

PAGE 60

ON YOUR OWN: $2.4 \times 1.8 = 4.32$ ft^2

PAGE 61

1. $4.2 \times 1.3 = 5.46$
2. $4.9 \times 0.2 = 0.98$
3. $5.03 \times 6.8 = 34.204$
4. $8.7 \times 0.13 = 1.131$
5. $8.1 \times 0.22 = 1.782$
6. $24.1 \times 0.14 = 3.374$
7. $1.32 \times 2.4 = 3.168$
8. $13.9 \times 2.7 = 37.53$
9. $4.8 \times 3.8 = 18.24$
10. 4.3 pounds/day $\times 7.5$ days $= 32.25$ pounds
11. $\$4.80$/pound $\times 3.25$ pounds $= \$15.60$
12. $\$9.30$/hour $\times 25.6$ hours $= \$238.08$
13. 4.2 feet $\times 5.1$ feet $= 21.42$ square feet
    21.42 square feet < 22 square feet; no

LESSON 27

PAGE 62

ON YOUR OWN: $3.5 \div 7 = 0.5$ yard

PAGE 63

1. $19.8 \div 2 = 9.9$
2. $7.2 \div 5 = 1.44$
3. $37.17 \div 9 = 4.13$
4. $493.6 \div 8 = 61.7$
5. $3.15 \div 7 = 0.45$
6. $356.2 \div 13 = 27.4$
7. $27.72 \div 21 = 1.32$
8. $150.6 \div 12 = 12.55$
9. $195.2 \div 32 = 6.1$
10. $\$150.00 \div 4$ days $= \$37.50$/day
11. 52.5 cups $\div 15$ batches $= 3.5$ cups/batch
12. $\$163.90 \div 22$ hours $= \$7.45$/hour
13. 16.875 ounces $\div 15$ pieces $= 1.125$ ounces/piece

LESSON 28

PAGE 64

ON YOUR OWN: $14.03 \div 4.6 = \$ 3.05$ per pound

PAGE 65

1. $367.2 \div 7.2 = 51$
2. $0.48 \div 2.4 = 0.2$
3. $9.8 \div 4.9 = 2$
4. $61.5 \div 12.3 = 5$
5. $9.72 \div 7.2 = 1.35$
6. $356.2 \div 1.3 = 274$
7. $2.100 \div 0.56 = 3.75$
8. $8.4 \div 0.42 = 20$
9. $5.856 \div 0.32 = 18.3$
10. $\$48.75 \div \$3.25$/pound $= 15$ pounds
11. 34.5 yards $\div 5.75$ yards/chair $= 6$ chairs

LESSON 29

PAGE 66

ON YOUR OWN: $\frac{6}{50} = 0.12$; $0.28 = \frac{28}{100} = \frac{7}{25}$

PAGE 67

1. $\frac{1}{5} \times \frac{2}{2} = \frac{2}{10} = 0.2$
2. $\frac{3}{4} \times \frac{25}{25} = \frac{75}{100} = 0.75$
3. $\frac{31}{50} \times \frac{2}{2} = \frac{62}{100} = 0.62$
4. $\frac{7}{25} \times \frac{4}{4} = \frac{28}{100} = 0.28$
5. $\frac{9}{10} = 0.9$
6. $\frac{7}{8} = 7 \div 8 = 0.875$
7. $0.08 = \frac{8}{100} = \frac{2}{25}$
8. $0.23 = \frac{23}{100}$
9. $0.03 = \frac{3}{100}$
10. $0.6 = \frac{6}{10} = \frac{3}{5}$
11. $0.4 = \frac{4}{10} = \frac{2}{5}$
12. $0.75 = \frac{75}{100} = \frac{3}{4}$
13. $\frac{6}{25} \times \frac{4}{4} = \frac{24}{100} = 0.24$
14. $\frac{7}{10} \times \frac{5}{5} = \frac{35}{100} = 0.35$
15. $0.55 = \frac{55}{100} = \frac{11}{20}$
16. $0.04 = \frac{4}{100} = \frac{1}{25}$

LESSON 30

PAGE 68

ON YOUR OWN: about 92 million; gradual, steady increase

PAGE 69

1. 300; find point for 10 AM; read across to scale at left.
2. 400; find point for 2 PM; read across to scale at left.
3. 7 PM; compare heights of points.
4. noon; look for highest point; read down to find time.
5. 10 AM; look for lowest point; read down to find time.
6. after noon; look for where line begins to descend.
7. 2 PM; line begins to rise again.
8. 11 AM and noon; find successive points with a noticeable difference in height; subtract lower point from higher one to find greatest difference.
9. 6 PM; find point for first hour; then identify point that is about twice as high.
10. 550; subtract 300 from 850.
11. 350; subtract 400 from 750.
12. 450; subtract 400 from 850.
13. 550; subtract data for lowest point from data for highest: $850 - 300 = 550$.

LESSON 31

PAGE 70

ON YOUR OWN: highest in winter, lowest in summer; higher in fall than in spring

PAGE 71

1. 2001; find highest point on line graph for prom.
2. 400; read across from that point to scale at left.
3. 2001; find highest point on line graph for homecoming.
4. 450; read across from that point to scale at left.
5. 1995; find year where two graphs intersect.
6. 1994; find year where point on prom line is above point on homecoming line for that same year.
7. 1998; look for greatest difference in heights of line for one year.
8. 1998–1999; find successive years where two graphs create a horizontal line.
9. 1997; find year in which both graphs descend from the year before.
10. 50; subtract 250 from 300.
11. +50; subtract 1998 homecoming data from data for 2001.
12. +150; subtract 1993 prom data from data for 2001.
13. no decrease; there was an increase.

LESSON 32

PAGE 72

ON YOUR OWN: 9 million fewer sales

PAGE 73

1. 175; find bar for coupes; read across to scale at left.
2. 100; find bar for sports cars; read across to scale at left.
3. mid-size truck; find tallest bar.
4. station wagon; find shortest bar.
5. 2-door coupe; find bar that is nearly twice as tall as that for sports cars.
6. 4-door sedan; find bar for trucks; look for bar that is about half as tall.
7. SUV, minivan, mid-size truck; identify all bars higher than 200 on the scale.
8. station wagon, sports car; identify all bars lower than 150 on the scale.
9. SUV; find the second tallest bar.
10. 75; subtract 75 from 150.
11. 290; add 220 to 70.
12. 200; subtract 100 from 300.
13. 330; add $150 + 180$.

LESSON 33

PAGE 74

ON YOUR OWN: watch TV; 5 more boys than girls chose
use computer

PAGE 75

1. sophomore; compare bars for popcorn tins.
2. $240; find top of popcorn bar for sophomores; read across to scale at left.
3. popcorn tins; find shortest bar for junior class.
4. $90; read across from top of bar to scale at left.
5. popcorn tins & box of fruit; find two matching bars for sophomores.
6. coffee mugs & mints; find set of bars in which the taller bar is the one for juniors.
7. box of fruit; find set of bars in which the bar for sophomores is about twice the height of the bar for juniors.
8. about $350; add $100 + $250.
9. about $150; subtract $90 from $240.
10. about $960; $240 × 4 = $960.
11. about $585; $195 × 3 = $585.

LESSON 34

PAGE 76

ON YOUR OWN: 125

PAGE 77

1. 35%
2. 15%
3. 10%
4. CDs and presents; compare percents shown for those two categories.
5. clothes; find greatest percent (or sector size) shown.
6. school supplies; find smallest percent (or sector size) shown.
7. clothes and food; find two percents that add to 50%.
8. presents, school supplies, CDs; add percents to get 25%.
9. $9; 0.15 × $60
10. $21; 0.35 × $60
11. $15; 0.25 × $60
12. $12; 0.10 × $120

LESSON 35

PAGE 78

ON YOUR OWN: drama

PAGE 79

1. sports; orchestra, chorus, band; speech, debate, drama
2. 376; read only the data in the circle for that activity alone.
3. 417; read only the data in the circle for that activity alone.
4. 234; read only the data in the circle for that activity alone.
5. 74; find the intersection of the two activities.
6. 98; find the intersection of the two activities.
7. 48; find the intersection of the two activities.
8. 23; find the intersection of all three activities.
9. 612; 417 + 74 + 23 + 98
10. 521; 376 + 74 + 23 + 48
11. 403; 234 + 98 + 23 + 48
12. 220; 74 + 98 + 48

LESSON 36

PAGE 80

ON YOUR OWN: 5 players

PAGE 81

1. 3; count the Xs
2. 14; find group with least number of Xs
3. 17, 18; find groups with same number of Xs
4. 18 & 19
5. 14
6. 19
7. 3; subtract 5 – 2
8. 8; count Xs for ages 14–16
9. 12; count Xs for ages 17–19
10. 20; add all Xs
11. 5; subtract 19 – 14
12. Answers will vary.

LESSON 37

PAGE 82

ON YOUR OWN: pass; positive

PAGE 83

1. car's age in years
2. car's value
3. $12,000; find lowest of the points for that age.
4. $19,000; find the point farthest to the right for that age.
5. 2
6. 2; fewest number of points
7. 9; add 5 + 2 + 2
8. less; $18,000 < $20,000
9. false; the older a car is, the less it costs, in general.
10. true
11. Generally positive; newer cars have greater values by and large.
12. $10,000 or less; 5-year old cars are valued at $11,000–$13,000.

LESSON 38

PAGE 84

ON YOUR OWN: 12

PAGE 85

1. 21; count the number of leaves.

2. 2; count number of leaves above row for stem of 2.

3. no; no leaves shown with stem = 8

4. yes; twice collected 71 cans—2 ones among leaves with stem 7.

5. 2; count leaves for stem = 10.

6. 6; count leaves for stems < 5.

7. 6; count leaves for stem = 7.

8. 78; add 35 + 23 + 12 + 8.

9. 315 (including 70); add 56 + 58 + 63 + 68 + 70.

10. 492; add 91 + 98 + 99 + 101 + 103.

11. 438; add 70 + 71 + 71 + 73 + 74 + 79.

12. Yes; add numbers already added in exercises 8–11 (minus 70, which has been counted twice).

13. Yes; 6 times students collected between 70 and 79 cans.

LESSON 39

PAGE 86

ON YOUR OWN: 7

PAGE 87

1. 55–57
2. 70–72

3. 4; find top of bar for the interval, read across to scale at left.

4. 61–63, 70–72; find bars with equal heights.

5. 4; read across top of bar to scale at left.

6. 67–69; find interval with bar twice as tall as bar for 70–72 group.

7. 64–66; tallest bar
8. 22; add 10 + 8 + 4

9. 8; add 4 + 3 + 1
10. 30; add 22 + 8

11. 26; think: 60 in. = 5 ft; add 4 + 10 + 8 + 4

12. 4 ft 7 in.

13. Yes; 30 on team, 22 are taller than 63 in.

LESSON 40

PAGE 88

ON YOUR OWN: 25%

PAGE 89

1. 2; check frequency for number of events = 0.

2. 2; check frequency for number of events = 5.

3. 6; look down number of events column.

4. 3; look down frequency column for greatest number.

5. 10; check frequency for number of events = 3.

6. 30; add numbers in frequency column.

7. 2; there are two events with frequency = 5.

8. 6; add 2 + 4.

9. 20%; find what percent 6 is of 30, or $6 \div 30 \times 100$

10. 15; add 10 + 5.

11. 50%; find what percent 15 is of 30, or $15 \div 30 \times 100$

12. 30%; add 5 + 2 + 2, then find what percent 9 is of 30, or $9 \div 30 \times 100$

13. Answers will vary.

LESSON 41

PAGE 90

ON YOUR OWN: 405

PAGE 91

1. 200; add 66 + 30 + 60 + 24 + 20.

2. 5; soccer, baseball, basketball, hockey, tennis

3. 10%; find what percent 20 is of 200, or $20 \div 200 \times 100$

4. 15%; find what percent 30 is of 200, or $30 \div 200 \times 100$

5. basketball; find the number that is twice 30.

6. 1,300; subtract 1,500 − 300.

7. 495; $\frac{66}{200} = \frac{n}{1,500}$
8. 225; find 15% of 1,500.

9. 180; find 12% of 1,500.
10. 150; find 10% of 1,500.

11. 450; find 30% of 1,500.
12. Answers will vary.

PAGE 92

ON YOUR OWN: Japan and Australia

PAGE 93

1. 35; read bar graph.
2. China; 32 is close to 35.
3. Russia; find total number of medals won, find 25% of that number.
4. Russia; read bar graph.
5. USA; find total number of medals won, find $\frac{1}{3}$ of that number.
6. Japan, Australia, China; read bar graph.
7. circle or bar.
8. line; graph needs to show changes in data over time.
9. China and Australia; find two countries that won more gold medals than silver or bronze medals.
10. 43; subtract 92 − 49.
11. about 40%; find about what percent 350 is of 929, or 350 ÷ 930 × 100
12. Yes; (16 + 16 + 38 + 14 + 29) > 100

PAGE 94

ON YOUR OWN: true

PAGE 95

1. B; difference in bar heights is greater in this graph.
2. A; subtract 75 − 0.
3. B
4. A; range of bar heights is small.
5. 5; 5 periods in graphs
6. 3; read either graph to find bars with heights > 55.
7. 1st; find class with shortest bar.
8. 12; subtract 75 − 63.
9. Answers will vary, but for accuracy of appearance, start scale at 0.
10. Yes; scores would look different because the bar heights would increase.
11. 12; subtract 63 − 51.
12. $\frac{51}{75}$ or $\frac{17}{25}$; in simplest form
13. $66\frac{2}{3}$%; $\frac{51}{75}$ is about $\frac{50}{75}$ (using compatible numbers), and $\frac{50}{75} = \frac{2}{3}$ or $66\frac{2}{3}$%.
14. 100%
15. Yes, but only if the intervals were changed.
16. Answers will vary.

112